To
my favorite
+ uncle!
Love, Barbara

blue shy

blue shy

BARBARA LINK

and other ways to spell hope

after brain injury

NORDTVEDT PRESS

Foreword

During one busy, as usual, Saturday afternoon, I read *Blue Shy*. It gripped my attention and I read it through in one sitting. I strongly identified with the narrator more as a parent than a neurosurgeon who often treats traumatic brain injury (TBI). I was completely caught up in the powerful story.

Blue Shy is a book that teaches. It is both a chronicle of injury and recovery and a metaphor for parenting. How much should we do for our children? How much do we let them do for themselves? This is a fine line all parents must navigate. The book is a lesson in dealing with one of the hardest things a parent can ever go through. It is a lesson in finding realistic parental expectations…having to come to grip with the fact that your child may never be "back to normal," and, finally, a lesson in how to release your child into the world again.

I was honored to be asked to write a foreword for *Blue Shy*. In its own special way, the book is a tribute to many of my patients and their dedicated families, and the organizations that support them, but most of all to the many young people who must reconstruct their lives after TBI. The incidence of traumatic brain injury is overwhelming, but *Blue Shy* gives us hope. I believe all who read *Blue Shy* would be uplifted by this courageous and touching story of a mother and daughter's triumph over adversity.

James E. Boggan, MD
Professor and Vice Chair, Neurological Surgery
University of California, Davis

For my daughter

Subj: Fog sky
Date: March 3, 1998
From: Else Ane
To: jenwrite@aol.com

Hi Mom,
It has been foggy this morning, but the wind is putting up
so maybe we will see some blue shy today.

Love, Ellie

blue shy

1

December 9, 1987, 7:30 p.m.

It's chilly tonight, our usual December weather in Merced, California. The tule fog has hung in the cold air all day, and now, when I poke my head out the front door, I can't even see to the corner. Even though it's Friday night, I'm satisfied to be cozied in my bedroom with my small electric space heater crackling and glowing like a real fire.

The phone interrupts my gift wrapping. I pull the twisted phone cord over my bed, scattering the books of poems I've written and am wrapping for Christmas gifts. I included a poem for each family member, and two for my daughter, eighteen-year-old Ellie.

On the phone it's my ex-husband, Gary. He's shouting. "Someone tried to kill Ellie."

"What? What are you talking about?"

"He attacked her." He yells again. "The sheriff from Colorado just called. She'll be calling back with more details."

"Oh, my God. I'll be right over."

I grab my car keys and purse. I back out of the garage without checking for traffic. The engine roars down the street because I forget to shift out of second gear. In my rear view mirror the yellow light from the open garage door fades into the fog. I'm not going back.

Earlier that day, I sent Ellie a Christmas package. A red turtleneck shirt, a Norwegian wool sweater, and heavy wool socks. Fiercely independent, she was camping out on the side of Kendal in the San Juan Mountain Range near Cimarron, Colorado, that summer. In the fall, she built a shack about a half-mile from the abandoned Kittimac Mill. Then, in late October, she moved to a rented room because of the cold and, as she told me, "Mom, last night a porcupine ate my tennis shoes!"

For the first time since the divorce five years ago, I enter Gary's house. Not the house we lived in, but a new one in a better neighborhood. The living room looks like Breuner's showroom: beige leather sectionals, giant stereo speakers, and leopard print pillows, a plastic palm. In the dining room rests the only familiar thing, the antique table and chairs that I lovingly refinished. The house smells like stale pizza.

I grab a phone in the family room and collapse into the beanbag chair to wait for the Cimarron call. The woman sheriff's tone is matter-of-fact and I don't even know what to ask; the attack is so hard to believe. In fact, I don't believe it. Ellie was a Tae Kwon Do fanatic. Who in a town of 515 people would hurt her? When she left for Colorado, I felt she had a new start working in a small town with two interesting jobs: a cook at the Silver King Bakery and a part time DJ at the local radio station.

Soon my sixteen-year-old son, Lars, joins us, as well as Andy, my boyfriend.

"Gary, you remember Andy?" I ask.

"Yes." Gary shakes Andy's hand stiffly. "Why don't you all have a seat?"

"Okay, thanks." Andy sits close and holds my hand. Andy and I are engaged and he's spent lots of time with both my children.

"Ellie can't be badly hurt," Lars says. "She's too strong. I'm going to call Cimarron, I know the EMTs." Lars and his girlfriend Josie were in Cimarron for the last two summers. His friend tells him that she fought hard when placed in the ambulance. We take this as a positive sign, although it was probably only a reflexive action. Toward morning, he sobs in my arms (the one and only time I can remember). He keeps repeating, "She's so good, who'd want to hurt her?"

Subj: too young
March 5, 1998

Hi Mom,

When I called my new Hospice person she thought I was too yung. "What can you do for me?" she asked. I told her I was a good lisner, could wash her dishes and clear her house.

Keith and I saw Kolya yesterday, it is a good movie, but the people were talking too fast for me to see the subtitles.

The phone rings again. It's the call we've been waiting for: Dr. Henson, a neurosurgeon at San Juan Medical Center, Farmington, New Mexico. Earlier, we had given permission for emergency surgery.

Gary and I each have phones, cords stretched from another room as we crouch on opposite sides of the beanbag chair. "Will she be okay?" I ask, my mouth pressed to the cold phone.

"She's been in coma since the debriding procedure to relieve the pressure on the brain. I want you both here as soon as you can make it. Fifty percent of the people with the injuries she's sustained die in the first six hours."

"Drive or fly?" I ask Gary in the three-way conversation. He fingers his clipped mustache.

"The flights are unreliable because of the winter weather. If you drive, take the southern route through Arizona." Dr. Henson sounds like a travel agent.

"Let's get off the phone and leave right now," I say.

"It's too late." Gary rubs his eyes. "I'll pick you up in the morning, early."

Back in my own house, in the garage, I locate the green suitcase with the broken handle in the garage and throw in sweaters, jeans, a ski parka, and hiking boots.

By four in the morning I'm packed, and it's too early to call my parents or make arrangements to leave my job or cancel my tennis game that afternoon. Dizzy tiredness forces me to lie down, fully clothed, on my bed. The breath is knocked out of me.

At 8 a.m. Gary still hasn't arrived and I call my office at the county where I work in the Social Services Department. I leave a message for my supervisor that I will not be in on Monday. Instead of calling my parents—my Mom will start to cry—I can't handle that, I call my sister who is a nurse and will remain calm.

"Jane," I start.

"Hi, sis, you're up early on a Saturday."

"Some bad news, I'm afraid." I keep my voice low and steady mindful of the way Gary tossed the news to me like a hand grenade. "It's Ellie," I choke up. "Just a minute." I take a deep breath like I'm going to dive under water. "Ellie's been hurt—some kind of attack. I don't know the details."

"Oh, how awful. Is she okay?"

"No. Head injury. She's just had surgery for a brain injury."

"Oh, no. What can I do?"

"I don't know—I can't think. Call Mom and Dad, call everyone. Pray."

"Are you okay?"

"I'm numb. I just want to get to her. Gary and I are leaving any minute. I'm waiting for him to pick me up."

"You and Gary are driving? Together?"

"Yes, that's the fastest."

"How's Lars? Shall I call him later? Oh, what hospital?"

"She was first taken to Durango, about fifty miles away, triaged and then when they couldn't treat her she was loaded back into the ambulance and taken to San Juan Medical Center in Farmington, New Mexico."

"Why there?"

"That's the closest trauma center."

"Call me as soon as you can."

"Okay. I think it's about a twenty-hour drive."

2

Eleven Hundred Miles

I'm trapped in the car with my ex-husband, driving from Merced, California, to Farmington, New Mexico. I never wanted to be with Gary again, but now I don't care how I get to Ellie as long as it's fast.

I take the first shift and speed down the Central Valley on Highway 99.

"Gary, remember this route? When we took the kids to Disneyland?"

"I remember the long lines. The heat."

"But we had fun. Jane met us there. She was working at Cedars of Sinai Hospital that summer."

"Did you call her?"

"Of course. She'll let the rest of the family know. But Ellie and the Matterhorn—God, I didn't know it was a roller coaster—I hate roller coasters. Thought it was a tour of the inside of the mountain or something. They put me in the front seat and Ellie behind me. She was only four. 'Purse between your knees, Lady,' the operator said. I felt like jumping off. The first hill scared me spitless. But Ellie was laughing."

"You shouldn't have let her go to Colorado."

"I thought it would be a new start for her. Lars found her the job—she would be in the mountains, camping. She said some of her friends were getting into drugs and she wanted to get away from that."

Miles go by in silence. I speed through Chowchilla and Madera. I see workers in the field pruning the grape vines, bundled up against the cold tule fog. Next it's Fresno and I feel like I'm making progress. Then Tulare and Delano and we're beyond the vineyards and into orange groves, pecan trees and cotton—crops that need the slightly longer growing season of the southern valley, as we discovered. We had planted a Meyer lemon when Ellie was eight. She took the first lemon to school for show and tell. But we forgot to cover it one cold night; the new tree froze and Ellie, tearfully, helped us pull it out in the spring.

I hazard a look at Gary. It's been a long time since we've been together alone. I'm remembering how we worked so hard putting in our first yard. First we scraped off the top layer of soil to get all the weeds out. The kids even took turns pulling the rakes. Then we planted dichondra, which grew lush and green. Should I talk or is it safer to say nothing? But he's asleep.

At Bakersfield the country changes again. Oil derricks pump up and down like the heads of donkeys. I check the odometer—163 miles closer to Ellie. I hold the steering wheel with my knees and consult the map. We'll cut across the California desert on Highway 58 to Barstow. By now it's mid-afternoon, the fog has lifted and I see white lines criss-crossing the blue sky. They're jet trails from the training flights over Edwards Air Force Base. I envy their speed. There's no traffic so I put my foot into it.

"Barb, you're going to get a ticket."

"A ticket? You're worried about a *ticket*?"

Gary carefully folds the map of Arizona I've crunched down between the seats and replaces it in the glove compartment.

"Hey, I need that map."

"Well, I'm not paying for the ticket, not even half."

At the next gas stop, Gary asks, "Are you hungry?"

"No, not really. I brought a few snacks." I rummage in my paper sack and remember how Gary hates eating in the car. "I've got cheese sticks, apples and crackers. Do you want anything? I won't make crumbs."

We snack carefully. I think of my own car with no eating rules. It's a mess with crumpled lunch bags, orange peels wrapped in napkins, empty styrofoam cups.

At Barstow we switch drivers on Highway 40, an Arizona interstate. I trace the route on the map with my finger. To the south is the Bullion Mountain Range and a Marine Corps Training Center. Then to the north I catch a glimpse of Table Mountain but it's too dark to see. I try to doze; when I close my eyes I see Ellie struggling in the ambulance and my eyes jerk open. At Needles we cross into Arizona. Five hundred miles closer.

The few towns on Highway 40 are Yucca, Kingman, and Seligman—all places I've never heard of. It's dark in the desert. Off in the distance I see a fire. At first I'm not alarmed then I see more and more—blue and yellow flames. I feel like we're driving into a kind of hell. Bonfires flicker, dim and brighten on the horizon like the Northern Lights I used to see when I lived in Montana. I turn to Gary, then realize, oil refineries. It must be the oil refineries burning the excess gas.

We drive on and on through the night, with the semi-trucks as our only steady traveling companions. They remind me of normal life—trucks carrying milk, apples, tires and furniture to someone's new house. Somehow, I find their size and speed comforting, as if I'm traveling down a long tunnel guided by protective elephants. I think of Ellie making us read *The Story of Babar* over and over.

Gary slows the car. I get mad. I swear I could run faster than he can drive. I watch the speedometer hover around forty miles per hour. Is he creeping along on purpose to torment me? Maybe he's just tired.

He insists on stopping at Jack in the Box in Kingman. He cuts, salts and chews each bite, looking at me as if cutting and salting are virtues I'll never understand. To keep from yelling at him, the drive is wearing on both of us, I dash to the pay phone, stand in the cold and call the hospital in Farmington. Ellie's condition has not changed.

Back on the road, the car is too warm and Gary's strong cologne gives me a headache. I crack the window and listen to the tires on the frozen asphalt.

"Have you heard of Frank Harmon? The man they arrested," Gary asks, breaking the silence.

"She mentioned a Frank who used to work at the radio station. He had been fired and came to the station stoned on pills in a suicide attempt. Ellie called the ambulance."

"That's sounds just like her. Helping some jerk."

"But how could she get hurt in such a small place? Wouldn't everyone know who the crazies are and avoid them?"

"It only takes one. Can you drive? I want to get in the back seat and nap."

At Gallup, New Mexico, we turn north and enter the Navajo Indian Reservation. The landscape is flat except for hoodoos, mushroom-shaped rock formations. The dwellings are sparse and interspersed with an occasional gas station and shabby souvenir shops. We stop for gas and I go around back. In the single restroom with a rusty toilet and no door I crouch to pee and gaze out over the windswept, barren land.

At Shiprock, the last town before Farmington, the signature rock formation looms like a lost ship. The hardened lava plug is three thousand years old and rises a third of a mile high. It acts as a beacon to lost travelers.

Finally, in the cold pink and orange dawn we arrive in Farmington. We've traveled eleven hundred and seventy eight miles.

"There's a Best Western. Let's get some sleep," Gary says.

"No," I shout. "We didn't drive twenty hours just to sleep. We're going straight to the hospital."

3

Helping Hands

Even in the soft light of morning, Farmington's a rough place. The roads are rutted with ice and gravel. Our tires slide at the stop signs. Hogans and tar paper dwellings make up the outskirts of town. We pass bars, a Mexican restaurant, check cashing places, pawnshops, and signs advertising bail bondsmen. I'm shocked to see drive-up liquor stores and drinkers passed out in cars in the parking lots.

Formerly a rich agricultural center, the Farmington economy is now based on the boom and bust production of oil and natural gas. I know what that means when I read it in the AAA book—a population of "roughnecks," as the oil workers are aptly called. No foreign or even new cars cruise the frozen streets, only muddy trucks with heavy studded tires.

The hospital stands out, a modern five-story building faced with gray stone against a grayer sky. We park close to the front in the almost empty parking lot. Bypassing the elevator, I dash up the stairs and hurry into the six-bed Intensive Care Unit. Ellie lies in the bed by the window. Her head is swathed in a huge turban of white bandages. Her face is swollen at least twice the normal size. Her eyes are closed and circled with purple bruises. There are tubes everywhere and the monitors are beeping. My eyes go out of focus and the turbaned figure in the bed wavers—it can't be her—I feel dizzy and start to fall. The nurse catches me as I slip to the floor.

After we spend the day at the hospital, Gary and I drag ourselves into the Best Western motel. We have two beds in a single room, as I can't afford my own. Since our divorce I've struggled financially, especially to keep our house. I felt it was vital that Lars and Ellie stay in their neighborhood school.

Preparing for bed, Gary paces around in his underwear and calls his girlfriend, stroking his imaginary beard as if he's a professor lecturing to his class. I wonder if it bothers the girlfriend, as it did me, to be called "babe."

Suddenly, Gary slaps a gun on the table between our beds.

"Where'd that come from?" I ask.

"I brought it from home. Kept it under the car seat," he replies. I flash back to the time when his hobby was gun collecting. He used to pour over the mail-order gun newsletter. Once the guns were in his hands he'd spend hours oiling and polishing them.

This gun looks like a World War II German Luger, but I don't know for sure. I turn my back and stare at the curtained window. The gun lies near my head, and when Gary leaves the room, I turn it so it points away from me.

During the night I hear yelling in the parking lot, bottles breaking, car doors slamming and a truck rattling away.

In the afternoon we meet with Dr. Lynn Henson for the first time. Unlike the gray-haired, distinguished neurosurgeon I pictured, he has a little boy face with round cheeks and wears cowboy boots. He tells us he was skiing with his children when he got the call from the hospital.

I start, "Can anything more—?"

"How does that CT scanner operate?" Gary interrupts me.

Dr. Henson blinks. "Computerized tomography, a three-dimensional image of her head."

"Oh, computers. How does that work exactly?" Gary's an engineer and seems ready to ask more questions about the equipment.

I interject quickly. "How did the surgery go and what can we do now?"

As we look at her films, Dr. Henson traces the numerous breaks in Ellie's skull with his surgeon's delicate touch. "Fortunately her skull was broken in so many places that her brain had room to swell," he says. "Otherwise, she wouldn't have survived."

I lean against the pale green wall. I've got cramps in both my toes from my tight boots. Later, I take the medical reports off by myself to read, my eyes swimming.

Closed head injury with multiple skull fractures, both linear and non-depressed as well as compound, comminuted, and depressed. The patient has a left frontal epidural hematoma, acute. Left cerebral contusion, possible right hemispheric contusion as well. Disposition: On the basis of the aforementioned x-rays and clinical exam the patient is to be taken to surgery for emergency craniotomy to evacuate the left frontal epidural hematoma and debride the compound depressed left parietal skull fracture.

The Intensive Care Unit works at a frantic pace. The nurses pull twelve-hour shifts and look exhausted. I'm surprised at the number of male nurses but can see they have the strength to move the patients. Sometimes I hear sharp words from the nurse's station and think the stress must be awful. I can come in and go as I please; no one pays much attention to me and I wander like a ghost. Gary spends most of his time in the waiting room, doing paper work and making calls. Mostly, I hover over Ellie leaving only for bathroom trips. I'm still shocked by her bandaged head, the purple eyes, and her pasty skin. Her hands are red, rough, and chapped from washing dishes and living outside. Caked blood lines her fingernails.

Standing by her bed, I feel so completely helpless. I have to do something. So I rummage in my purse for an emery board and toothpicks. I clean under her nails with the toothpicks and file away the rough edges. Then I dash downstairs to the gift shop and buy some peach-scented hand lotion. I rub her hands—first one then the other. I scrutinize the green lights on the monitors and tuck the white flannel blanket up around her neck.

"Mom's here," I whisper, "here to take care of you." My voice is weak and trembly. There is no response.

Seeing her so quiet and still is new to me. At six weeks she bobbed her head around to see everything, her bright eyes much like a baby bird. We called her "turkey neck."

At five months, she hooked her hands in the sides of her net playpen and pulled herself upright. As a toddler, her goal was to get into her older brother's room. One night I heard a bump, bump, bumping. Streaking down the hall I found her thumping her head against her brother's door. Another night she did get in his room and played at stacking his cardboard blocks.

Subj: no words
March 9, 1998

I have been waffling on my Hist 5 paper. I need to write more than 750 words on how I really did not have a clear opin on this subject! Do you think I just made things harder than they need to be?

I get the Dutch Baby recipe you sent but have not made one yet. I do not have a soufflés dish so can I use foil around a shorter dish?

In the morning I notice that Ellie's not the only one in the ICU. In the next bed lies a nineteen-year-old, a victim of a car accident. As a result of an injury deep in his brain stem, he curls in a fetal position. Since he's wearing only a kind of diaper I notice his smooth brown skin and black curly hair.

He's aspirated into his lungs and is on a breathing apparatus. His parents stand close, their knees touching his bed. His sister sings to him, her hands clasped in front of her like an opera singer. She has a beautiful voice, and I hope Ellie can hear her, too.

A doctor I don't recognize comes in the unit.

"Hi, I'm Dr. Weisner."

"Ah—nice to meet you. Are you a neurosurgeon?"

"No, I'm a family practitioner here in Farmington. I used to practice in Merced. My niece called and said you were here. I wondered if I could help?"

"Thank you." I couldn't think of any questions for him at that moment. "I think everything's being done that can be done. We're just waiting at this point."

"No, I meant for you. What can I do for you?"

"Well, I can't sleep. I think about her when I go to sleep and when I wake up my first thought is Ellie—it's like I haven't been asleep."

"Here's a prescription for sleeping medication—Dalmane. It'll be good for about four hours."

"Thanks." My throat is so tight I can only squeeze out one word.

The phone in the waiting room rings constantly, mostly for Gary and me.

"There's no change," I report to the family and friends.

My friend Alan, a pediatrician who diagnosed Ellie's thyroid condition, calls from home.

"How is she?"

"No change. Coma."

"What's her number on the coma scale?"

"I don't even know what that is. But I'll check."

"Less than six is pretty dicey. There could be a long recovery if she comes out of it and lasting disabilities. Do you want me to consult with someone in Neuro?"

"Please. Anything you can find out."

Alan's the first friend not to say she'll be all right. I welcome his honesty.

Back in the room I check her chart and read the stats. I can see that the Glasgow Coma Scale measures Ellie's coma—a coincidence since I grew up in Glasgow, Montana. It assigns points from three to fifteen. The criteria are eye opening, verbal responses, and motor responses. In eye opening, she has one point for never; in verbal response she has one point for none, although earlier in the ambulance and the emergency room in Durango she had moaned; in motor responses she has three points for flexor response. Her total is only five or six. The nurses test her frequently with a pinprick on the bottom of her foot; I wince each time.

The newspaper reporters I've been dodging catch up to us in the hospital cafeteria. "Was Harmon her boyfriend?"

"Of course not! She was only trying to help him. Did you know she's left-handed? She's proficient in Tae Kwon Do. She worked as a cook and counselor at YMCA Camp Jack Hazard in the California Dardanelles." I go on and on—can't stop talking. "She took the bus to Colorado for the summer and camped out alone on the mountain while working at the Silver Mountain Bakery and the radio station. She moved indoors only because of the cold weather and when she discovered that the porcupine had eaten her shoes." I stop out of breath.

"Babe, you handled the interview well," Gary says.

Subj: no subject
Date: March 11, 1998

I have called the rehab office a few times but Martin is not caling me back. I think he does not have a real job for me. With my funny speech I guess I can't be a radio announcer like I did in Colorado.

Did I tell you mediCal will only pay for the tooth to be pulled but what will I do for a bridge?

Ellie's been in coma for ten days now; has added a point or two on the Coma Scale. Mostly in motor response, still no sounds or eye opening. My mood swings wildly; one minute I think she'll recover fully and basically there's nothing wrong. In the next, I picture her in coma for years. According to the booklet the longer the coma, the more severe the disabilities.

Snowflakes ping against the ICU window as I read Ellie a letter from Blake in Merced. It's signed, "Your Friend Forever, Blake Lewis." Ellie and Blake have been close friends for years and took Tae Kwon Do classes together. They even developed their own elfin language. I tape the letter to the wall with the rest of the mail. While I'm reading, I think, *Babar, the Elephant.*

"Babar and Celeste come to Farmington." I improvise. "They peek in the hospital windows looking for you, and scare the other patients."

It's very quiet after my story. The monitors beep, and Ellie breathes softly. Just as I waited for the doctor's call at Gary's, and just as I waited during the car trip, I hold my breath now and wait. I wait for the world to right itself.

I wait for Ellie to wake.

It's my eighth day in Farmington and Kim and Wayne wait for me outside the ICU. They've heard about Ellie.

"I brought you a booklet on head trauma (see appendix A) that really helped me. I got hurt on Wayne's motorcycle," Kim says. "My speech is almost better. And," she brushes her hand through her short blonde hair, "my hair is growing back."

"Do you need a car while you're here?" Wayne asks.

"Yes, I really do, how did you know? Ellie's father left for California this morning and my boyfriend won't be here for four or five days."

"We heard you were alone. The car is a dark-blue Chevy—parked out front. It is Kim's car—pretty wore out but okay around town."

"I don't know how to thank you—for coming to the hospital, the book, everything." I'm overwhelmed with this unexpected help.

I am alone for now and recall how Gary and I said good-bye that morning at the hospital.

"I have to get back to work," he said. His shoulders were hunched and he had bags under his eyes. I realize he's as exhausted as I am.

"Okay—when you come back—I'll go home and make arrangements for Ellie to come to California." We've agreed to work in shifts. Although we're cooperating for the moment, the stress of being with him and trying to remain disengaged exhausts me.

Just last night I waited outside the ICU. He asked if he could be alone to say good-bye to Ellie. The neon lights in the green-walled corridor were dim and a faint beeping was the only sound. It was restful like a dim, cold sea.

Bursting out of the unit, Gary shoved his face close and yelled, "This is all your fault! You never taught her to wear makeup." Stunned, I crouched with my hands over my face. I didn't get up until I heard his boots stalking away.

Now, with the one bad tire bumping on the snowy road, my loaner car gets me back to the motel. Alone, I scan the head injury book, which details the eight levels of cognitive functioning. I think of Ellie groaning and struggling in the ambulance—sounds like *Level II: a generalized response when a patient reacts inconsistently and non-purposefully to stimuli in a non-specific manner. She has a long way to go.*

Will she wake up, and if she does, what will she be like? Will she be able to think, speak, and take care of herself? It's almost Christmas and I remember the cold, foggy Christmas Day I ran beside her in the street as she tried out her new bicycle. I held onto the seat as she pushed the pedals and wobbled forward.

Today, the fourteenth day in the hospital, I receive a message about Ellie from a woman on the first floor named Margaret. How did she know? The Farmington grapevine, I guess. I take the stairs two at a time down to her room. She's a tall woman with rumpled gray hair and watery blue eyes. The hospital gown reveals bony shins in need of a shave.

"Ellie's an angel," she says. "Let's pray for her." She raises her hands in the air like she's a charismatic. I feel self-conscious but think 'what the hell'—as I follow her lead.

"Father-Mother-God, we lift up this angel to you. Hold her in your hands, hold her—heal her. Bring her back to us. We will love her and never leave her. Amen."

"Amen," I whisper.

"Where are you staying?" Margaret asks.

"At a motel."

"I just had an emergency appendectomy. Not a small thing when you're fifty-eight. It will be a while before I can work—I'm the head janitor at San Juan High School. Been there for thirty-five years. I'd feel better if someone was in my house. Would you want to stay in the back bedroom? I can't take any money for it."

I shove my hands in my Levi pockets, "You're so kind. Everybody here—" I choke up.

"Here are the keys. I'll write the address. From here it's only five blocks." Her hands are red and rough with knuckles the size of quarters. I'll bring her some of that peach hand cream.

"I'd love to stay in your house. Let me know if there's anything there you want me to take care of."

It's my new life. My past life in California—the poetry books I was wrapping for Christmas gifts lie scattered on my bedroom floor, the unwashed clothes fill the laundry basket, the mulberry leaves pile up in the yard—trivial details of my past. And I refuse to think about the distant future. All that matters is that I have a place to stay and a car to take me back and forth to the hospital—to Ellie.

Subj: Stormly windy day
Date: March 12, 1998

Keith is unhappy about living with me as a roommate. It has been making me feel sad because he is unhappy and that means I will lose my home here. I love living in the house. It is so quiet, the neighborhood is security and at night I do not worry about people breaking in. All I can do is to wait until Keith decides, I feel sorry for Keith, but his in-decide does make me world that stable, but that is life.

I'm waiting in the cafeteria for Andy to arrive from Merced. I'm hungry but don't want to sit still long enough to eat. I put the broccoli soup and salad on my tray. The salad croutons are stale and hard. It's starting to snow and the cold air is coming in around the window.

Even though Andy looks tired he still has the rising-on-his-toes-bouncy step—almost a swagger. His faintly equine face gets stares from the other diners. I forget just how handsome he is. He hands me a copy of *The Merced Tribune*. The lead article tells the gruesome story, "Hammer Attack on Local Woman." Funny, I never think of Ellie as a woman. I hate the unsmiling picture of her they run with the article.

I remember when her picture was in the *Tribune* two years ago. The occasion was an eight-week Tae Kwon Do class held in Legion Park. Ellie had been doing Tae Kwon Do for about three years. Her brother, father and I were avid tennis players. She chose martial arts instead. To accomplish her practice goals, she rode her bike to the Army surplus store and purchased a used duffel bag. She stuffed it with old clothes and strung it up on our patio. I watched her from the kitchen window as she spun and kicked, spun and kicked, over and over, until she got it right.

The two-year-old picture of Ellie in the *Tribune* is titled, "Kickin' around in the park." In the photo she wears her karate outfit and kicks high. It's on a picture perfect California day, 82 degrees.

———————

Subj: teeth trouble
 March 14, 1998

I met my Hospice person (Joanie) today. She wants me on Thursdays so I can clear her bathroom and vacuum her home.

After two appts for a root canal, I have only one nerve in that tooth. So it's been quiet this week, I think it's trying not to give me pain so I won't have it drilled out.

Thanks for telling me to use spell check on my e-mails. Even tho I go to college, my brain doesn't spell anymore.

Andy and I go to Margaret's house. It's freezing after we close the storm door. I turn up the heat. In the hall, we gaze at her pictures. A young dark-haired woman stands by a sailor. I don't see any pictures of children.

"Good, you have a bed," Andy says as we enter the back bedroom.

"Where will you sleep?"

"On this." Andy carries an egg-crate mattress he's found discarded at the hospital. "You know I can sleep anywhere."

"Okay, put it right by me, then."

He flops it on the floor beside the bed. "Oh, oh, I'll be lower. Will the lower bed give me lower self-esteem?" He's referring to some terms from our couples' counseling. Then he starts his laugh—a long red-faced wheeze followed by heh, heh, and heh. Suddenly, I'm so glad to see him. I hug him and he pulls me on his lap and I sink my face into his neck smelling the starch and soap and feeling his gray and black curly hair. But I can't have sex—I'm completely numb.

Andy and I pray with Margaret every day. The same routine, hands in the air. I'm starting to like this new way of praying. It opens my chest and I breathe deep. Margaret asks Andy to plant some bulbs in her front yard. Daffodils she didn't get in last fall. He digs in the frozen ground while I stay at the hospital all day. He insists that we go out for dinner every night. Mostly we eat at the Mexican restaurant. The chili rellenos are stringy and full of seeds, the enchiladas dry as toast so I settle for the chicken tacos and have them every night. I don't care about the food; after three bites I'm filled up, then I feel safe to sit and let myself cry.

Andy has his camera and takes pictures of Ellie in her hospital bed. I can't imagine why we want to record any of the horror but he says we'll want pictures later.

One afternoon, he makes me leave the hospital to visit the Anasazi ruins some sixty miles away in Chaco Canyon. In the park, we drive on a long dirt road to see the twelve hundred year-old prehistoric Indian remains. We climb into the snow-dusted Pueblo Bonito, the site's largest remaining kiva. We're the only tourists at the site and it's easy to imagine the ancient Indians planting corn, weaving fabric and carrying out their sacred ceremonies. Later, we browse the gift shop and talk to the park ranger. I buy a book on the Anasazi for Andy's mom.

"Do you like this?" Andy picks up a thin silver necklace with turquoise beads. I hold it around my neck and look in the mirror and see how weight has dropped off my face and neck.

"I like it."

On the way back to the hospital I stroke the necklace; the silver is soft and cool in my hand.

Subj: Tue. & Thurs.
Date: March 23, 1998

Last week seemed to go by fast! I saw Joanie on Tue and Thurs.
On Tue I cleaned her whole apartment and she told me that on
Thursday she wanted me to do some ironing. But when I came on
Thurs she first told me she wanted her apartment to be cleaned
first and she left the apartment. Then her daughter (Kate) came
within 15 mins. and told me that her Mom is not remindering
things and showed me how to iron. Joanie came home and Kate
tried to have her Mom eat some soup but Joanie started to choke
and cough for about 20 mins It almost made me cry when I saw
Kate trying to help her Mom stop coughing. Kate and Joanie were
standing up and Kate was holding Joanie's shoulders because
Joanie was too weak to stand and cough at the same time without
falling. There is a very strong different between a healthy person
and a 80-70 pound dying person.

Today Andy and I drive to Cimarron to get Ellie's things from her rented room and go to a benefit dinner for her. To Lars, his friends and Ellie, Cimarron must have represented the free, independent and pioneering spirit. I read in the AAA book that this area of the San Juan Mountains in Colorado was first occupied by the Anasazi Indians and later settled because of the rich silver mines. The Cimarron Railroad connected the mine sites and Cimarron became the county seat around 1876. In the 1960s and 70s it became a tourist attraction and most of the silver mines had been shut down. Young people flocked here to staff the restaurants, bars, and to hike, climb and bike ride.

We stop to look down into the town surrounded by spectacular snowy mountains. The sky is such a bright blue I can barely keep my eyes open in the glare. "Wow, now I know why Lars and Ellie loved it here." I want to just look and not get back in the car. "It's gorgeous," I say, and Andy agrees.

The benefit for her recovery fund will be at the Silver King Bakery. I'm anxious to see where she worked. Outside is a chalkboard that reads: Today 1:00 to 7:00, Benefit for Ellie. The menu features fried chicken, potato salad and baked beans. Half of the bar revenue goes to the fund, as do all of the dinner sales. A large chalkboard on the wall announces a benefit raffle for Ellie. The prizes are all donated from local merchants: a Standard Metals mine tour, a half-day jeep rental, a brass oil lamp from the candle shop, an electric can opener, dinner for two at the Silver King Bakery, a calculator from the Cimarron Standard, a case of pop from the 8 Ball (a local bar), a marble vase, a rental ski package for 2 from the ski shop, a 14 lb. turkey from the Lake St. Market.

The Silver King dining room has a high ceiling, a handsome wooden bar and is well heated with a large wood stove. I'm eager to peek in the kitchen where she worked, and find it well equipped with a walk-in cooler, large commercial ovens, and a special pastry mixer. The dining room is charmingly decorated with colored lights and a large Christmas tree. The people I meet are warm and cordial, and are concerned about Ellie, although, no one talks about the attack itself. I remember the sheriff had gone right to where Frank lived with his mother. My one silent question is: how did they know to go after Frank?

The day has a somewhat festive air, people helping people. It seems important to record this outpouring of kindness for her, and Andy takes pictures of Ellie's friends, the hundred-year-old brick buildings that line the street, the snowy mountains. I feel thankful that she has good friends and made a life. However, my spirits plunge when the UPS truck arrives at the bakery as we're sitting down to eat.

The deliveryman carries in the package asking, "Is there an Ellie Jensen here? There was a note on her door that she works here." It's the very same Christmas package that I carefully wrapped and mailed to her two weeks earlier from California.

After the benefit, I want to find her camp on Kendall Mountain but the snow is too deep. The mountains remind me of taking our kids camping. We had another family (with three girls) that we often went with; one time the camp ranger in Big Sur admonished us when we were jumping rope. "You're too loud," he said. "Stop having so much fun."

On our camp-outs, Ellie loved to gather treasures. At the beach she would run ahead of us picking up shells with her pigtails bobbing like Pippi Longstocking, a character in her books. Somehow she knew not to pry living starfish or anemones from the tide pools. She cried if I didn't let her take all her treasures home. I always brought a bag just for her special rocks and shells. I still had a paper sack in her closet full of dried, smelly shells and beach rocks.

Since the mountains are too snowy to search for her little camp, we walk around the corner to the radio station. The owners wait for us by the now locked front door.

"How is she?" The owner doesn't quite meet my eyes. He lights a cigarette and throws the match on the ground.

"About the same. Still in coma."

His wife pulls her parka together as the zipper is broken. "We're sure sorry."

"Do you want to look around? This is the reception area. Here's the control room," the owner says.

It's quite small, really, a shoestring operation: one long room with the reception area in front and the control room around a counter in the back. I glance at the control panel, the cords and switches, a pair of headphones and turntables, but look away when I picture Ellie on the floor tangled and bleeding.

"Here's her last paycheck." He hands me an envelope and I cram it in my pocket.

After the radio station we walk the half block to get her things. Her tiny rented room is freezing. I shove her backpack, radio, sleeping bag, *The Lord of the Rings Trilogy* (still open to page 283) and clothes into black plastic garbage bags. Her underwear is shabby and that makes me cry. I sit on the floor weak and shaking, unable to continue. Andy quickly finishes the packing and we leave.

4

High Tops

Linda, my friend from our Bag Ladies Writing Group, calls to tell me her brother-in-law, Carl Swenson, is an attorney in Denver. He invites us for Christmas. I don't want to leave Ellie. I'm not anxious to meet new people and can't imagine celebrating Christmas. But Andy presses me to go. It's only about an hour's flight from Farmington, and Andy in his usual generous way, buys the tickets and makes the arrangements. Ellie is getting good care and won't know I'm gone for two days. She is still unresponsive.

Before we leave I talk with the doctor. "Her feet are turning inward," he comments. "Can you get her some high-top tennis shoes?"

The next afternoon, right before our flight to Denver, I go to K-Mart. In the shoe section, I am confused, can't remember her size. I wear a 6 ½ and her feet are bigger than mine. I ponder the selection, unable to make a decision. I remove my boots and start to try on. I sit on the wet and muddy floor with a pile of tennis shoes around me.

A woman clerk arrives. "Can I help you?" She's old enough to be my Grandma and her dowager's hump protrudes from her blue, nylon smock.

"I'm looking for some tennies for my daughter. High-top."

"We don't have much selection in the winter."

"She needs them to keep her feet from turning. She's unconscious. Up at the hospital."

"Oh, I read about her in the paper—the one in the coma. My name's Betty. What's her name again?"

"Ellie."

"That's right Let me see here—what size does she wear?"

"I can't remember."

"Well, I wear an eight." Betty holds out her foot. "Does this look right?"

"I don't know."

We try on the shoes—stand up and walk around. Then Betty puts on a pair of lavender heels.

"What about these? Are they the right size?"

We laugh. "Well, what about these?" I roll up my jeans and slip into gold, strappy sandals. Then Betty finds wedgies, red with high heels. She ties them on and sits down kicking both legs in the air. Her legs are mottled with blue veins— banana-bread legs, my mother would call them. Soon we're clomping in men's work-boots and fuzzy pink slippers and laughing hysterically.

I feel I've slipped down Alice's rabbit hole. It's Christmas Eve. I'm sitting on the floor at K-Mart trying on shoes for my comatose daughter.

Subj: more problems
Date: April 4, 1998

I'm applying for low rent housing if it doesn't work living with Keith. So I need a copy of my birth certificate. I hope you and Andy are working together so life will be better.

I think I'm starting to get another yeast infection and I need to go to my clinic. You may not think a yeast infection is not much but if you ride a bike each day, having it is on your mind much more!

Christmas Eve, 1987

It's even colder in Denver and reminds me of the severe winters in Montana where I grew up. The car windows are frosted; the exhaust system puffs white smoke when Carl and wife, Anna, pick us up at the airport.

The Swensons are just starting their Christmas Eve celebration when we arrive at 6:30. They welcome us like family members. Christmas Eve dinner is a Swedish smorgasbord; it's the first time I've had lingonberry crepes. They taste tart like tiny cranberries. Later, Andy dresses up as Santa and distributes the gifts to the children. He's so convincing no one can figure out who he really is. The Swenson children, Cody, their four-year old son, and baby Ingrid, are delighted with Santa. Later, most of the adults go to church but I take my pill and go to bed.

Christmas morning we open presents. Fur-lined leather gloves and perfume for me and a plaid wool neck-scarf and pipe tobacco for Andy. Carl, Anna, Carl's brother and wife play Trivial Pursuit off and on all day. I don't want to play but I like to listen to their voices.

Before we leave we talk about the legalities of the case. Late on Christmas Day we also consult a worker's compensation lawyer as the attack happened when Ellie was at her job at the small radio station in Cimarron. Carl Swenson agrees to take her case.

On the return flight my tears exempt me from conversation. Andy chats with our seatmate.

"I'm on my way to my new job as Sears credit manager in Farmington."

"Is that right?" Andy says.

"Yes. I hear Farmington is the best kept secret in the Southwest," he remarks.

I can't wait to get out of here and take Ellie home.

Subj: too long
Date: April 23, 1998

The check should be written to Humboldt Open Door Dental Clinic for $430. I think you would need to write a note with the check saying the money is for Ellie's New Crown.

Today was the first time I saw Joanie (my hospice person) and her daughter together without being very angry at each other! Joanie has always been very nice to me, but she cannot talk that much and she is angry at that, and because it is taking too long to die, and she does not want to die this way. At the same time Kate is very angry because her Mom is dying and she wants to help (but what can she do?) but her Mom just nags at her and Kate has two small boys.

5

Waking Up

Back in the intensive care unit a new patient arrives, a big burly man with a face that looks like a squashed plum. He was sledding and hit a truck. He watches us from his bed and doesn't seem to have any visitors.

Ellie is still very pale. But her chin and cheeks are more defined as the swelling is subsiding. Now, I can recognize that little face I love so much.

In the two days I've been gone I notice a big difference. She's coming slowly awake. Her number is higher on the Glasgow Coma Scale. I'm so excited when her eyes open a little, then disappointed, when they flutter shut. She doesn't speak or follow commands. *Level three: patient reacts specifically, but inconsistently, to stimuli.*

The bruising around her eyes is turning yellow and green and her hands are soft and clean. She moves her feet restlessly in the tennis shoes I got before Christmas. They fit pretty well. I'm beginning to feel real hope. I hold her hand tightly.

"We'll be home soon," I promise, "pretty soon."

"Her brain swelling is going down." The doctor is making his rounds. "I have to say again that she was lucky that her skull was shattered in so many places. It gave the brain the necessary space to swell. The hematoma in the frontal lobes resulted from the impact of the hammer sending the brain thudding against her skull."

I wonder if she screamed for help?

We decide to transfer her as soon as we can make arrangements, to the spinal injury unit at San Jose Valley Medical Center for intensive rehabilitation. I'll drive ahead and Gary will return and stay with her until the plans are complete and she's ready to travel.

It's the 18th day since Ellie was attacked. She partially opens her eyes and smiles a lazy, lopsided smile when she sees me. God, that smile! It's really Else

Ane in there! Instantly, I recall a baby picture, her hair brushed in a curl on top of her head, a ball in her tiny fingers and that same big, juicy smile (she was such a drooler). I hug her tightly and cry, only stopping when the doctor comes in the room for an exam. She moves her left arm and leg in the bed but her right side is paralyzed and she doesn't speak.

"Can you squeeze my hand?" the doctor asks. And she does.

"There will be a lot more improvement," he says.

I'm so excited that I want to run and get the camera and record everything, just like when she took her first steps.

We move her from the intensive care unit to the surgical floor. I untape her cards, letters and telegrams and take them to the new room. She is still wearing the high-top tennis shoes but I can see that they are loose on her feet; she has lost weight.

We take turns feeding her soft foods and she is my baby again. I remember the day she was born. I had only quit my clerical job four days before and was home cleaning our 10' x 30' student-housing trailer. As I stretched to get a box from under the bed I felt my water break. Gary dropped me off at the hospital and went on to take one of his finals. By the time he got back, maybe three hours later, Ellie, impatient to be on her own, was born. When I held her for the first time she was a damp, warm bundle and her face was red and squished. I was euphoric that I had a healthy baby girl.

Now, I take the spoon and circle it around in the air, "Zzzzzzzz. Here comes the bumblebee. Open up." And I zoom the bite into her mouth. She tries to smile around the food and we lose most of it on her chin.

Subj: Dutch Baby
Date: May 3, 1998

I made my first Dutch Baby. I used 1/4 cup of butter, 1/2 cup of flour & milk and three eggs. It turned out fine but Keith likes brown sugar with the dutch baby more than powdered sugar. They did not have the tools to work on my root canal in DDS office so they made me wait 45 mins then cleaned my teeth.

I've been trying to read "Tales of beauty: A Woman's exceptional life" by Alison Rose in the New Yorker. I get mad when I buy the magazine but can't read. My allergies have been very light now.

6

No More

Andy and I start back to California in his Volkswagen Rabbit. I hate to leave but Andy has several projects demanding attention in his architectural office. Also I'm almost out of sick leave at the county. When I kissed Ellie good-by, I told her we would see her in California. I hold her medical reports on my lap and I read to myself as we drive.

> The patient is a well-developed, adequately nourished, Caucasian female who is semi-responsive. She moved all extremities spontaneously, however, she had marked right hemi-paresis. She would occasionally moan or groan but otherwise there was no speech or attempts at communication. The patient would follow no commands.

"Andy, this report sounds awful."

"You don't have to read it." He reaches for my hand. "That part is all over now."

"I feel like I need to understand her injury to help her get better."

"How about reading it to me?"

"Okay, here goes.

> She had a bilateral hemotympanum. The scalp was swollen and tense over the entire left hemicranium. There were two 1 1/2 inch long parietal scalp lacerations. Inspection of the same revealed a depressed comminuted skull fracture immediately beneath. In addition there was quite a large left sided battle sign.

"God, Andy, what the hell does 'battle sign' mean?" I'm feeling angry and it feels good to feel anything other than despair. "Is that a special medical term or evidence that there was a struggle?"

"You know Ellie. I'm sure she fought back." Andy's voice calms me.

"Shall I go on?"

"Sure," Andy answers.

Back and extremities-Notable for an ecchymosis over the left shoulder and several small area of ecchymosis on the dorsum of the left foot.

"That doesn't sound too bad." I leaf through the pages. "Oh, here's an explanation of the operative procedure, I'll read that."

The entire calvarium was clipped with an electric razor. The left side of the scalp was shaved with a safety razor and her scalp closely inspected. This ecchymosis of contused area on closer inspection was, in addition to the underlying fracture, a round area of ecchymosis or contusion an indentation almost the outline of the head of a blunt object such as the head of a hammer. The margins of the laceration were rather sharp, that is they were not avulsed or torn but rather had been split rather cleanly by the force of the blow. The entire scalp was covered with dry blood. The comminuted area was impacted with hair and some scalp and there was considerable coagulated or congealed blood throughout. This was removed by irrigation, the hair was carefully removed and meticulously picked away from all the exposed area of calvarium so as to prevent subsequent infection.

"That's it." I toss the report in the back seat. "No more."

Subj: Some Days
Date: May 10, 1998

I get a subscription free for life from the talking books each two months, it has a listing of new books put on tape. But I do not know if there is a book club here for me to join like you mentioned. I have been hearing a book called, ALL QUIET ON WESTERN FRONT. It is a good book but I had to stop the tape because I was too sad. Some days are better than other days.

"I'm thinking about getting Ellie a headband. An Indian headband," I say. "Can we stop somewhere?"

"A headband?" Andy rubs the whiskers on his chin. "What for?"

"She's going to miss her braid. It was so thick and long. That pitiful bald head. Besides the stitched wounds, she has a large depression on the left side."

"Can't that be fixed surgically?"

"Later. And that small bone loss area can be filled in."

"That should take care of it. And her hair will grow back."

"No, really, I want the headband. Stop at the next souvenir shop?"

"Do you really thinks she needs it?"

"What about the women that have lost their hair in chemo after breast cancer treatment?" My voice is shrill.

"Okie, dokie."

In Gallup we hit the big time for gift shops. I trudge from shop to shop on my headband mission. At the Fifth Generation Trading Company, I get distracted by the rugs and fold them back, examining them one by one. How thick and warm they are! I move on to the scarves and headbands: turquoise, orange, red, purple, brown, black bands. Long bands and short ones with knotted fringe. I hesitate as Andy waits by the checkout. Finally, I select three headbands— a black and brown in a geometrical design and the other two in red and orange. On the way out, I grab a pair of turquoise and gold earrings.

"She'll need these, too."

Back in the car I spread the headbands over my lap and meticously adjust the distance between them. I wind the fringe around my fingers, feeling the rough weave. I pull down the mirrored visor and wrap the red one around my forehead. Then I roll them carefully, wrap them in tissue and replace them in the gift bag. A wave of depression hits me—the shopping frenzy is over. Why did I think a brightly colored headband would help a head injury? Ellie's not going to want to wear an Indian headband. At the next rest stop, Andy goes in for coffee, I remove the earrings and toss the bag of headbands in the garbage.

I take over the driving so Andy can rest. After fifty miles I notice the gas gauge is on empty and we are in Arizona desert late at night. Please, God, please, no more. As we crest the top of a hill the motor coughs and sputters, then stops. We roll down a steep hill and off onto an exit ramp and into a large Chevron station where several semis are gassing up. The gas station feels like a little miracle and I feel hope again. Leaving the station I glance in the rear view mirror; I've forgotten to replace the nozzle. It yanks out of the tank and is flipping around on the ground. Andy wakes up to see my take-off. We both laugh, I don't go back; a gas cap is the least of my worries.

Subj: Freedom!
Date: May 22, 1998

Well I think I understand why Andy went to work right before you were planning to clean the upper windows; it take too long to clean windows and right after you are finally done (after many hours) you start to see all the spots that you miss the first time but at that time you have run out of newspaper or Windex! I can't wait to see The Lost World with you.

I take my final history test on Monday, so my summer has begin. What is the dates that you and Andy will be here? I need to plan my trip to Oregon. I saw 'Gross Pointe Blank' movie yesterday, it was cute because of John Cusack's acting, but the second movie was much better, it was called 'The Day Trippers,' Did you e-mail me that you saw that movie?

7

Breaking Away

Andy and I wait excitedly at the airport in San Jose, California, as Ellie arrives today from Farmington. I haven't seen her for two weeks. In that time she's been making good progress—moving to commands, recognizing her Dad and nurses, attempting to feed herself and standing up with help. I called her every day and she smiled into the phone, the nurses said, but didn't speak. From Farmington she has been flown over the mountains in a single engine Cessna. The money from the benefit in Cimarron pays the $1600 for the plane ride.

She has ridden on a narrow stretcher in the back of the plane—about the space in the back of a station wagon. Pulled over her bald head is a purple ski hat and she clutches a teddy bear and waves and smiles when she sees us, as if she has been on a big adventure. I wonder how she kept warm going over the mountains. She is weak but can do a kind of shuffle when we support her on both sides.

We guide her into an ambulance, get her settled on a stretcher and follow in our car to San Jose Valley Medical Center, and settle her in the two-bed room that costs $1800 a day. Luckily, her Dad has gotten her on his insurance. I talk awhile to her roommate, Lillian, an elderly woman with very white hair who seems interested in Ellie.

I meet her doctors and therapists, her team at this teaching hospital. Although I've returned to work, I drive to San Jose one night during the week and both days on weekends. It's a two-hundred-mile round trip. I'm anxious for her to complete the recovery course here and return home so I can be with her full time.

By now, Ellie is mobile in a wheelchair. She doesn't speak but gestures to her head wildly with her left hand. I know she's asking how she got hurt.

"An accident," I answer. She pantomimes riding a bike. "No. Not a bike or motorcycle. Another kind of accident." I put off her questions. I remember *Level V: patient is confused, inappropriate, non-agitated and has gross attention to the environment, but is highly distractible and lacks ability to focus.*

"Should I tell her what happened?" I ask the doctor.

"She's not going to remember the attack." The doctor says. "She'll probably lose the whole week before."

"Do you know where this is?" I ask as I hold up a note card with Colorado printed on it. She jerks her thumb to the east. I'm excited; she can read at least one word.

In the mail this week, I receive a smudged envelope, addressed to me in childish handwriting. I rip it open and instantly figure out it is from Ellie's attacker. My heart pounds as I stick it in another envelope, seal, stamp it and take it to the post office. I can't bear to read it. So I mail it to our attorney in Denver. Then I imagine Frank Harmon coming to my door and ringing the doorbell. I knock him off my step. I punch and kick him and when that's not enough I tie him to the back of the car. I pull him behind the car like Dad used to pull us on the toboggan. I imagine the snow and gravel banging against his face. I drive and drive.

Today Andy tells me his cousin, Chuck, is in the same hospital as Ellie. We go together to meet Chuck's wife; she looks tired. I recognize the I'm-still-perky-despite-all-this-shit smile. We visit him in his room on another floor. His parents are staying in a camper in the hospital parking lot. Chuck's a schoolteacher in Merced and was hit by a drunk driver while riding his motorcycle to school. He is paralyzed from the waist down and is very depressed. His ward is full of people with spinal injuries. Some of the patients are strapped to boards called striker frames. They have no ability to move on their own. I talk to one young man who was hurt while skiing. Another fell off a ladder while washing windows and operates his wheel chair with his tongue. My eyes are opening to how dangerous daily life can be. I realize just how lucky Ellie is.

Subj: happy father day
Date: May 21, 1998

You did not nag me the other night on the phone I called the state rehab. he said he will call me when he gets the report from Redding, and then he said that will be in about the 23th of the month. Part of one of my tooth fall out last night; it is from the tooth that I am

have a root canal done on OR it is from my wisetooth next to 15.
We'll see where it is from on Monday at 9:30. Happy father's day
to Andy.

January 18 and I'm in my cubicle at work.

"Barbara, you have a call on line one. The hospital in San Jose." The
message is from one of the secretaries in my office. I feel icy calm when I answer,
gripping the phone, what now?

The nurse reports that Ellie keeps trying to leave the hospital in her
wheelchair and once she got to the street. To prevent her escape, they put a long
pole on the back of her wheelchair so she can't go through the ward doorway. Also,
part of the time they have to put her in restraints. I'm furious, because, I know
that means a strait jacket. I refer to Level V in the head injury book, which says
management on the ward is often a problem if the patient is physically mobile, as
he may wander off, either randomly or with vague intentions of going home.

At lunch I speed home and call the hospital. "Lillian, this is Ellie's Mom.
How are you?"

"Still here."

"Ellie's had some trouble. She tried to leave the hospital."

"Made it far as the street. God bless her."

"She has to stay in the hospital."

"I know that. She's here now."

"Do you think you could keep an eye out for her? Call me if you need to."
I give her my number. I'm desperate asking an 83-year-old woman to watch my
girl. "I think the nurses aren't watching her too closely. I really need to be there all
the time, but can't figure out a way."

"The nurses don't do diddly-shit. I'll do my best."

The next visit, I ask Ellie what she's going to do if she gets out of the
hospital. She jerks her thumb east to signify hitchhiking.

"What will you do when you get to Colorado," I ask? She punches the air
in fury with her thin fist. I think her dad must have told her who hurt her.

Ellie is undergoing intensive therapy: physical, occupational and speech.
She's making progress in all areas despite her sometimes-uncooperative attitude. At
the age of four months Ellie grabbed on and held her own bottle. She pushed away
the bottle if I held it for her. And then two months later she gave it up entirely and

would only drink milk from her cup.

On report day, family members, doctors and therapists sit around a huge table. Gary takes a seat next to Jody, the attractive patient coordinator with the long dark hair.

"Ellie only uses a tiny bit of toothpaste on her brush," the occupational therapist reports.

"Really?" I answer. "That's how she always brushed her teeth."

"I thought she didn't have the hand strength to squeeze the tube," the physical therapist says.

"Nope. She never did use much toothpaste." I feel like Ellie has won a tiny battle in her struggle to recover.

Later in the therapy room on a red plastic mat I help Ellie stretch her right side, which is still partially paralyzed. She pulls her leg back from my grip and tries to do the exercises herself. I've been worried what her new personality would be like. It's just like her old one, I'm happy to see.

When I push Ellie back to her room after therapy appointments, she has a visitor. It's Steve, a casual friend of hers from Cimarron by way of Australia. He wears a brown leather jacket over his strong shoulders and carries a motorcycle helmet. He has driven Ellie's motorcycle out to California. She had purchased it from him just before her accident, but never got a chance to ride it. I can't imagine anyone coming over the mountains on an open bike in January. But he's tough and even camps out in the hospital parking lot for a few days. I offer my house or to pay for a room.

"No thanks, mate," is all he says.

"What a hunk," I remark to Ellie, and she nods her bald head.

Subj: thanks
Date: June 3, 1998

Thanks You for that great visit!!! It was very nice to see you and Andy for a few days! Did Andy like that chocolate I got him for his birthday? I lived through my root canal apt. this morning. DDS said that the other dentist in Cedarville had been just stopping that infection in that tooth and did not start a root canal.

I will tell you when I get my women's bike saddle. I understand why those bike gloves are not longer available, it was a very good deal! After your weekend in Super 8, I think you may understand why I did not want to have an apartment in low-income housing. In the past there has been problems with the other people living next to you, who somehow do not sleep and play their TV or radio 24 hours a day. I was up at 4 a m this morning and the body told me it wanted to sleep in, but it always feel good after a workout at the gym! I hope you and Andy had a good workout in your gyms. Thanks again.

Tonight, January 30, here in Merced, is a benefit concert for Ellie at a local bar/restaurant where she used to work as a prep cook. The flyer reads, "Caring people for Ellie." The admission is free, but donations are greatly appreciated. The money will go into the fund for Ellie started by my son's girlfriend, Josie.

The evening is a blur of kind faces, music and food. A lot of my poetry friends attend, as well as people I knew from California State University, Stanislaus.

"Yes, she's hospitalized in San Jose and undergoing intensive therapy. Her right side is still partially paralyzed and she uses a wheelchair. We can take her out of the hospital to local restaurants and the beach." I keep repeating the same information.

An English instructor, Hayward, writes a check for her fund. "Remember when we took the girls to San Francisco? Kathy says to tell you hi and Ellie, too."

"The Mu Shu Pork. You had us try it. I still love it." Hayward and I dated for a while right after my divorce. Sometimes we included our daughters, both fifteen.

"Kathy's in her second year at San Diego State. And she just got engaged."

"Great." I say it with little enthusiasm as I picture the differences between our daughters now. Later, in the bathroom, I check to see if there is handicapped access at this restaurant. Yes, we could bring Ellie here. But what would it be like for her visiting a restaurant in a wheelchair where she used to streak around, cutting veggies and stirring delicious soups?

Subj: dying soon
Date: June 23, 1998

Remember Joanie my Hospice client? Her daughter Kate is not
taking her Mother's sickness and soon death very well. I am sure
she is doing a better job then I would if you were sick. If Joanie tells
me to iron, Kate tells me not to. I think she is unconsciously trying
to control her Mother so Kate can stop her Mother from dying. But
she cannot do that, no person can, it is just life and sometimes it
hurts.

The microwave you gave us stopped working; just like Keith and I.
Should we take it in for repair or what?

The hospital has a halfway house we can reserve on weekends where
Ellie can stay with us. Andy and I make plans to go. He continues to be there
for me—driving me to San Jose, taking us out to dinner. He listens to me, non-
judgmental of my ups and downs when I rant about Gary or feel like discussing
Ellie's treatment.

Gary calls me at work about the arrangements for the halfway house.
"I'll go this weekend. You can go the next. I don't want to run into you and that
worthless son again."

"What on earth is going on?" I ask Dave during my counseling session. "I
can't believe he's acting this way especially, now when Ellie needs us the most."

"What happened at the hospital?" Dave asks.

"Not at the hospital but the halfway house last weekend. Gary and Lars
got in a fist fight. It was after they'd been out to a restaurant where Gary introduced
Ellie to the waitress saying, 'This is my brain-damaged daughter.' Lars asked Gary
never to call her that again, and of course, Gary tried to punch him.

"How did Ellie react?"

"She lurched out of her wheelchair and hid under the bed."

"Gary's still angry about the divorce."

"But that was five years ago."

"He's saved it all up and is dumping it on you now. Can you both come
in?"

"I'll try."

I make the call as soon as I get home. "Gary, it's Barb. I've been seeing Dave Shafer, you remember the counselor we saw when we were getting divorced. He thinks we need to work together now for Ellie. He wants us to come in together."

"He just wants our money."

"I'll pay."

"I'll think about it." He slams down the phone.

We all feel sad and ripped apart. Soon it'll be time to bring Ellie home, what then?

8

Home at Last

March 15 and Ellie is finally home. She can get around fairly well without the wheelchair, has some right side weakness, can dress and feed herself, but her speech is slow and hesitant. I remember how she wanted to take Latin in high school and now, she can barely speak or read English. "Dad," she says to me then shakes her head no. "Friend," she says when some welcome home flowers are delivered to the front door. Expressive aphasia is the medical term.

I catch her trying to throw her anti-seizure medication into the kitchen garbage. We are trying to get her off the medication since she has never had a seizure; it makes her extremely groggy but we don't have the doctor's okay yet. Her records are being held up at San Jose Valley Medical Center because the resident hasn't finished her release summary. Ellie is also suffering from extreme dizzy spells, apparently nerve damage. When I'm in her room, I witness one of her dizzy spells. I help her down to her bed and hold her still. I can see her eyes jumping behind her closed eyelids. She's miserable. Should I get rid of the waterbed—is it too jiggly? One time, I think Ellie was fifteen, I saw her sitting with her boyfriend on that same waterbed. Shortly after that cozy scene (I liked her boyfriend, he had dark curly hair and dark eyes and was studying Shakespeare with her) I thought I should talk to her.

"Sex happens," I said, "even when you don't plan it. If there's even the slightest chance something might happen, I'll get you on the pill. I don't think you want to get pregnant and an abortion would be an awful thing for you to go through."

Should I have told her about my own experience: pregnant and miserable at eighteen? I did not. She didn't respond to my talk with anything other than that teenage-know-everything look. What went wrong, I think? I wonder if the accident would have happened if I'd been a better mother?

Now I see her picking up books and staring at the pages from my homemade brick and board bookcase.

"Li-li-bary," she attempts.

"Good," I answer. "Let's go to the library."

Once there she goes to the philosophy sections and opens books that she used to be able to read.

"Mom, I-I can't."

"Not yet." I try to console her. "You have to re-learn how to read."

It's heartbreaking to watch. Later, on the way home she directs me by pointing to the turn for Woodrow, her old elementary school. I leave her in the car, her hat pulled down over her face, and borrow beginning readers for her to study. These readers are the same ones I brought home when Ellie was a third grader having difficulty learning to read. Every night, we'd sit on her bed and work together, although we didn't make much progress. Luckily, Mrs. Aoki, her teacher, had a solution. She let Ellie sit anywhere she wanted in the classroom—under her desk, on her desk, in the corner on the floor. And she encouraged her to make cups of tea before she started her reading. In a short time, Ellie was reading beyond her grade level. All she needed was to make her own way.

At the grocery store I browse in the books and magazines to see if there is anything that could help her. While I'm waiting in the checkout line, a small child, maybe six or seven, picks up a book and reads to her mother fast and clear.

A good friend of mine, Judy, agrees to care for Ellie during the day while I'm at work. Judy, a former co-worker at the Social Services Office, is a large woman with a huge spirit and kind heart. Sometimes, the two of us, at work, would get to laughing especially about my inability to understand percents and the tears would roll from her blue eyes. Judy has since left the county offices and is between jobs. She'll charge us only $100 a week, which we will pay out of the benefit fund; most important, Ellie likes her. I hope she'll have more luck than I have getting Ellie to cooperate with her treatment.

I make Ellie's favorite foods: killer burritos with shredded beef, pork chops with peaches and rice, cherry pie.

"You have to eat something," I say. "You're way too thin."

Ellie pulls her hat over her face.

"Just try a few bites."

"No." She pushes me way. Later I hear her crying in her room.

Judy arrives every morning in her old Toyota with her two dogs, Wally and Lady, who chase each other around the yard as I leave for work.

Besides her various appointments for intensive speech and physical therapy, I set up counseling sessions for all of us: Ellie, Lars, myself and her father. Ellie meets with Dave, the counselor, alone.

"She's suicidal," Dave tells us.

"Maybe that's why she's not eating. What does she say to you?" I ask.

"Oh, she doesn't talk to me. She draws pictures of guns and knives. You need to lock up all your sharp knives. Do you have any guns in your house?"

"No," I say.

"I have guns. Wouldn't be without them," Gary says.

"Take them out of the house. She's very determined." He looks at Gary. "Or at least lock them up."

I take all the sharp knives in the house, shove them in a paper bag and lock them in the trunk of my car.

I'd like to avoid the subject of suicide altogether but decide to talk with her in the best way I can.

"You're making such rapid improvements. I know you're going to get a lot better. Please don't hurt yourself, we all love you so much."

She takes me in her room and opens a library book on self-defense. She shows me pictures of self-defense moves and I read in one of the captions that a failure to protect oneself should, by some ancient code, result in a deserved death. I'm sweating during this conversation trying to say the right thing. But I know her reasoning is impaired and think that if we can keep her alive long enough, maybe she'll want to live.

"It's not courageous," I insist, "if you hurt yourself. In fact, it's way braver for you to live than to die."

Later, I take her out to buy a record album she wants. She tells me she'll pay me back and it seems important to her so I agree. Once home, she crouches in the corner of her bedroom in tears. She is painfully thin, a baseball cap on her shaved, scarred and misshapen head. I feel even more helpless than when she was in coma. What can I possibly do now to help her get her life back?

9

Goodbye to All That

Subj: like me
Date: July 12, 1998

I finished reading "Goodbye to all that" by Robert Graves yesterday, have you read it or some of his poems?

I finally read this book called THE GATE TO WOMEN'S COUNTRY last night, it was kind of sad. The women lived in towns and the men lived outside the town as warriors. The main person in that book was a girl-man who got a head injury by a man somewhat like mine. The women needed to have a blood clot taken out too The author was born and always lived in Colo The book was out in 1988, I wonder if she had read about mine head injury in Colo?

Tonight at 11:30 p.m. I get up out of bed and put on my old blue robe. I slip out the sliding glass door and sneak to the front yard trying to look in Ellie's bedroom window. She wants to be left alone but I have such a feeling of dread. I stand on my tiptoes, almost falling into the mock-orange bushes, to peek into her room. I see her baseball cap on the bed but that's all.

I consulted with her speech therapist, Jemma, today.

"No, she doesn't do her speech exercises," Jemma reports. "Instead, she sits and cries. But at least she feels safe with me. I hope she'll start working in time."

I'm feeling pretty hopeless, too, just like I did when Ellie was a sophomore in high school. She was going to her classes but just slouching at her desk—not participating or doing any homework. At home she was sullen and wouldn't tell me what was wrong. In fact, she was hardly talking to me at all. I would lie awake in bed and wait to catch her as she went down the hall to her room. But she would push by me and firmly close her bedroom door.

Dave, the same therapist we have now, was counseling me then.

"Give her some choices," he said.

"You can stay in school and participate, move in with your dad, or get a job. What sounds right? Think it over. I'd like for you to stay here and keep going to school."

She chose to move to a small apartment and got a job as a prep cook at a local restaurant. Then I didn't see her every day like I did when she was home. I would go around to her apartment on my lunch hour, my heart pounding, wondering what I would find. Mostly she wasn't there, so I explained the situation and asked her landlord to try and watch out for her. Gave her my phone number at work and at home. Frequently, I'd eat at the restaurant where she worked and slip into the kitchen to see her. A few months later she decided to go to Colorado. I loaned her the money for the bus fare. Could Gary have been right? Should I have insisted she stay in California?

Ellie's co-worker, Garrett, arrives from Cimarron to see her. His curly brown hair frames a boyish face and he is just Ellie's age. Garrett worked with her at the radio station and Ellie tells me they were just friends, not romantically involved. In fact, it was Garrett that noticed the radio station was off the air during Ellie's shift. It was around 6 p.m. and he came immediately to the station and found her in a pool of blood.

Garrett is English and pronounces each word with precision and elegance. He and Ellie ride bikes and watch TV. I'm worried about the bike riding. Ellie's skull has a round spot of bone loss. I strap her helmet on tightly when they go out. Ellie's helmet is loose but she looks cute in her shorts and red t-shirt. I snap a picture of them standing with their bikes in front of the garage.

"Quit that!" He tickles her when they watch TV. "Stop," she says. They chase each other around the house like a couple of cats. Garrett helps her with her speech exercises and goes with her to her therapy appointments. He sleeps on our convertible sofa bed and offers to help me prune the mock orange bushes.

When I see them together like normal teenagers I slip into a fantasy. Garrrett will stay in California and find a job at a local radio station. Ellie will continue to get better and better and take courses at the community college. In time they will marry—Ellie will wear a simple but elegant wedding gown and we'll all go to England together to meet his family.

Subj: Women
Date: July 17, 1998

This is from The Second Sex by Simone de Beauvoir: "But the women's effort has never been anything more than a symbolic agitation. They have gained only what men have been willing to grant; they have taken nothing, they have only received. The reason for this is that women lack concrete means for organizing themselves into a unit. They have no past, no history, no religion of their own; and they have no such solidarity of work and interest."

I don't think that is so true.

◆

Garrett finally leaves on March 10. I'm worried because I notice that Ellie is getting depressed again. Garrett has provided only a momentary distraction. She slouches on the couch when it's time to go to go to therapy and doesn't eat much of the meals I fix.

"If you lose any more weight, I'll hospitalize you for intravenous feeding," the doctor warns her.

Andy says he has something for me. "Here, Barb, here's Ellie's braid they cut off in the emergency room." He hands me a package wrapped in newspaper. "The doctor in Farmington gave it to me."

"You have her braid? Why didn't you tell me?"

"You wouldn't have wanted to see it then. I've washed out the blood."

"Thanks." I look at the braid: thick and brown, tied with a black hair band. "You know, the gold nugget earring she was wearing is still missing."

"*Someone's* wearing it," Andy says.

Should I return it to Ellie? I end up tossing the braid, enclosed in a plastic bag, on my closet shelf.

Gary and I sit on opposite sides of the waiting room before our counseling appointment. When we go in Dave's office, Gary raises his arms and backs away from me in mock alarm.

"How are you both doing? This is unbelievable stress you're all under.

Gary," Dave says, "let's start with you. What are you feeling today?"

"Piss poor. She's stealing." Gary's voice is shrill and he gestures toward me. "Stealing from Ellie's recovery fund."

Dave swivels his chair to face me. "Of course I'm not," I say. "How can you say such a thing? I've only used the money to pay Judy Richards to stay with Ellie during the day and take her to therapy. And because she's such a good friend, she's only charging us one hundred dollars a week."

"How do I know what you're using the fund for?" Gary shouts.

"Gary, I know you're angry but you need to stop the attack," Dave says. "Who's managing the fund?"

"Well, no one's managing it, really. Josie, Lars's girlfriend, set up a bank account with my name and hers on the account."

"Can you get someone not in the family to administer the funds?"

"We're only talking about $1400 dollars here. But, yes, of course."

"Gary, what do you think of someone you both agree on to administer the funds?" Dave asks.

"Anyone but her," Gary says.

"What if I ask Dennis Fisher? He's a family friend," I suggest.

"Gary? Does that work for you?" Dave asks.

"I suppose."

"That's a good compromise." Dave says. "Gary, can you call him? And let me know by next week's session. Barbara, can you stay for a minute?"

"Sure."

"And Gary, I'll see you next week. Please give me a call if you need to before then."

After Gary leaves I sag into the cushions. "Did I tell you Gary took a gun to Farmington?"

"Do you take Ellie to his house?" Dave asks. His deep-set eyes are darker and more intense than usual.

"Yes. I take her to visit."

"Gary's not in good control right now. I suggest you take someone else along when you drop Ellie off and pick her up."

"Good idea," I answer. "He's so angry."

Today I leave work early and drop in on Ellie's session with Jemma. Ellie's pushing letters around on a scrabble board when I get there.

"How are things?" I ask.

"Okay. Ellie's working hard. Glad you stopped in. I've heard good things about a residential head injury recovery center in the Bay Area. Here's the phone number; I think it would very helpful for Ellie."

I call and find out it's an all-inclusive program with only ten to twelve patients living together in a house. I'm excited, as Ellie has always loved Berkeley.

"What do you think?" I ask her.

"I—WANT Berkeley!" She is clear on this.

"Let's check it out. Find out what it costs and if the insurance will pay. I'll miss you here but I bet a full time program would help you make progress."

Ellie slumps in the car seat. "It's too hard here."

I call Gary and he says he'll check with his insurance.

Ellie looks thinner but weighs the same at her medical appointment on March 13th.

"Can you take off your shoes?" The doctor asks.

Her tennis shoes drop to the floor. Heavy, she has stuffed them with fishing weights.

"I'm going to hospitalize you if you don't eat," the doctor says and writes something on her chart. But she nods to say she'll eat.

She is mad at me all the time now and keeps her baseball cap pulled low over her eyes as she slouches around the house. I have read that head injury patients easily lose control over their emotions but my feelings are still hurt.

This morning in the kitchen, I say, "You have to eat some breakfast." She tries to slug me, misses and rams her fist hard into the cabinet. Then she stumbles to her bedroom and holds the door closed. I hear her crying.

I think back to Ellie's 7th grade graduation. I wanted her to wear a dress and took her shopping against her will. Actually, we always had monumental struggles when it came time for new clothes, new school clothes. She favored jeans and t-shirts and I wanted her to wear the preppy look. It got so bad that at the mall I decided it wasn't worth the battle so I said, "just pick out your clothes and I'll go back and pay for them." But for the graduation, I insisted and she walked across the stage in a simple dotted-Swiss summer dress with a fitted bodice and a long skirt. She was beautiful with her long brown hair and elegant dress but while in line she caught us admiring her and gave us a small fist shake.

"Gary, how's it going with the insurance company and the recovery center? Ellie's getting desperate—I don't know what she'll do. She keeps trying to run away from Judy."

"If you don't want her with you, she can stay with me."

"That's not it at all. It's too hard for her here, depending on us, reading like a third grader and being treated like a child when she used to be on her own."

"I'm negotiating with the insurance people about the cost of the program in Berkeley. They're hard-nosed sons of bitches."

"But Ellie doesn't understand the delay; she wants to go right now."

I give her the clean, washed braid. Her reaction is strange; she looks at her hair as if she has a plan.

On March 15th, Judy, Ellie and I drive to Berkeley to check out the Bay Area Head Injury Center. It is a foggy day in the valley but Berkeley is sparkling with cool sunshine. Students whiz by on bikes. We drive by the long-haired street vendors in tie-dye and long hair. I admire the blooming rhododendrons. Ellie leans forward to take it all in. She likes what she sees.

The Bay Area Head Injury Center is a large three-story house with a welcoming porch. We meet the director, Dr. Gregory, who has a slight stutter and a kind face.

"This would be Ellie's room and her own bathroom." He shows us a first floor room with a French door and large window. The walls are sage green set off by white moldings. "We all work together here like a family. She'd be expected to help cook and plan meals."

"Great," I say. "She worked as a cook at Y camp and has restaurant experience, too. She makes great soups."

"Chili," Ellie says.

"What about her therapy?" I ask.

"Some we'd do here. Some would be off-site."

"Do you have a van?"

"No. Several of our residents take the bus. Ellie could probably do that. Here's Marti, one of our counselors, who'd be working with Ellie."

Marti's a skinny little thing who looks too young to be a counselor. She and Ellie go off to look at the room again. When they come back they're giggling and Marti's wearing the joke glasses we were fooling around with in the car.

The whole set-up seems ideal and we stop at Zachary's for a spinach/garlic stuffed pizza; Ellie eats two pieces.

Subj: Bamboo & Butterflies
Date: July 28, 1998

"Strangers in a strange land," describes the book I'm hearing, BAMBOO & BUTTERFLIES by Joan Criddle. On the back of this book they said: After suffering incredible hardship and deprivation under the Khmer Rouge's regime, the four daughters of matriarch Ean Bun, their husbands and children, arrive in california with few possession, little money, and almost no understanding of their adopted country." After reading that book I am able to see our culture from a different perspective: I wish all grade schools will read that book to their students!

I am not sure if I will be able to drive to Sac. after visiting Lars & Josie it may be too warm to drive on Highway 5 to Merced with no AC in my car.

Ten days after the trip to Berkeley we are in an uneasy holding pattern. Gary says he's negotiating with his insurance people. Ellie is angry and sad. Her speech seems better, a little less hesitant and she compensates for her loss of names by saying my brother instead of Lars.

"When can—I go?" Ellie asks me every day. She goes into her room at night and locks the door. I hear her throwing stuff around and wonder what's happening. I practice unlocking the door of my room by inserting a hairpin into the lock in case I have to break into her bedroom. Nightly, I patrol her window to watch her movements, although I can't see much. I am relieved when her light goes out so I can stop window peeking and go to bed.

I'm so tired at work from my nightly vigils that at break I go to the downstairs ladies room for a rest. I lie down on a hard plastic couch, put a sweater over my eyes and fall dead asleep for twenty minutes.

"She ran away me from me today. I'm older and fatter," Judy chuckles, "but I caught her. I think we need to talk to her."

"Ellie?" I ask. "Where do you want to go?"

"Why does she go?" Ellie flaps her arm at Judy.

"Judy's here to take you to your appointments and help you during the day," I answer.

"I hate her."

"So if you were alone for awhile, where would you go?" Ellie points to her colored pencils.

"Hobby shop?" I ask. She nods her head. "I think that's okay. What do you think," I ask Judy?

"Everybody wants some time to themselves," Judy replies.

"Berkeley—?" She asks every day not understanding the delay. I don't understand it either. I suspect this is a power play by her father.

———————

Subj: Angry
Date: August 4, 1998

Sorry to hear you have the flu. I was feeling wretched all weekend and I thought it was because of the stitches & bleeding gums but on Monday I was able to correlate the Penicillin and my body's reaction to it. I feel worse because I was unable to clean Joanie's apartment that day. It always makes me angry when my body breaks downs because of colds, flues, or allergies because I need to help her.

It happens while I'm at lunch and I hear when I get back to work. My supervisor is a slow-moving guy who wears a flat top like he did in the 1950s. His stomach hangs over his belt and his keys jingle on his belt as he strolls to my cubicle. He coughs a phlegmy sound and his face wrinkles into concern. "Your daughter is at the emergency room at Scenic General."

I can smell my sweaty underarms as I call the hospital.

"She has had a recent head injury," I tell the emergency room personnel. "What's her condition?"

"She has slit her wrists and neck and has lost a lot of blood."

"I'm on my way over."

I quickly call Dave and I say in a shaky voice, "Ellie cut her wrists and neck with an Exacto knife. She's at Scenic General."

"I'll meet you there."

Another hospital, another emergency room. My knees feel like pudding when I enter the emergency room. I sink into the nearest chair. Ellie's neck and wrists are heavily stitched and bandaged. Her face is beyond white. She won't look at me. Dave talks to her and then to me out in the hall.

"She told me it was because she couldn't get into the Berkeley Head Injury Recovery Center."

"I guess I'm not surprised. I knew something was going to happen."

"You know, if she ever does succeed in killing herself, you aren't to blame," he says and puts his arm around me.

Ellie is out of danger and being kept overnight.

Subj: Beauty again
Date: August 8, 1998

I feel better now after no more penicillin. I like your last moral in that story from the New Yorker: True Beauty is something you may need to overcome! I saw the movie "Anna Karenina" I enjoyed it but it is a tragic love story so your heart is broken at the end of the movie and you paid 3.75 to have it broken!

I'm planning to drive to my brother's for a visit. It's better if I'm away from Keith for awhile. He isn't accepting that I'm not his girlfriend anymore.

I was at the gym today and it seems that I have lost about 2 pounds from the weekend! I was at Joanie's yesterday and it looks that she has lost weight too.

I drag myself home from the hospital. "What happened?" I ask.

Josie looks upset and angry. "Judy needed to do some errands so I stayed. I was studying out in the backyard. I called to her and got no answer. So I went inside. I found her in the hall bathroom. She'd cut her wrists—long ways and across her neck from ear to ear. She was over the bathroom sink so she wouldn't get the floor bloody."

"How'd you get in? Was the door locked," I ask?

"No."

"I suspected she was going to try something."

"Me, too." Josie starts to cry. "I should have watched her closer."

I give her a hug. "It could have happened with anyone—it's not your fault! You've done so much to help her—the fund, staying with her, cooking meals. You actually saved her by calling 911 so quickly."

"How is she?" Josie's brown eyes look huge in her pale face.

"She's lost a lot of blood but she's out of danger."

"But why—I don't understand—she's making so much progress."

"She's frustrated about not going to Berkeley. And she's pretty impulsive right now. Can't control her emotions."

"I've only tried to help but I didn't do much good." Josie turns away. I gently take her arm.

"Oh, yes you did—the fund—raising that money. It really helped. We could hire Judy. You've been a big help to Lars. You've stayed with her all those times when I was at work and Judy was busy. She will be grateful later."

"I've put all the towels in the washer. I should go to work."

"Right now? Are you sure you're okay?"

"No, I don't know—I can't get that horrible picture out of my mind—her bleeding over the sink."

"She doesn't know what she's doing."

After Josie leaves I give the bathroom sink another wipe. I yank the clean towels out of the washer and stuff them in the dryer. Then, I call Gary. He's back at work after going to the hospital.

"What about Berkeley?"

"Barb, I'm still negotiating with the insurance company."

"Time's up," I slam down the phone.

Subj: No Subject
Date: August 19, 1998

I'm ready for my trip to Oregon. Your package came this morning, I have plenty of dried fruit and $$. Thank you very much!! My stitches in my gums are healing just fine but, I was an unhappy camper yesterday when DDS Shell gave my gums a shot of novocaine before he put in a term. crown on #15. I was beginning to feel my gums and #15 after an hour and a half when I was riding my bike to Joanie's apt, but when I begin to clean her apt I forget the pain in my gums! There is no comparison between healing stitches in your gum pain and the pain of dying of cancer. Talking with Joanie give me a clearer perspective on life.

Today Ellie is discharged from the county hospital. However, because of her suicide attempt, the law says she has to go for observation to the lock-up facility next door.

"Do you want to go with me?" I ask Lars.

"Sure." Lars shoves his hands in his pockets. He sounds tense.

It's a Central Valley early spring day. The air is soft. Across the street from the facility is a cemetery—the large trees sprout spring green leaves. We squint our eyes in the bright sunshine as we walk between buildings.

Inside, we walk down a dark hall and come to her room on the left. Seeing her through the tiny window in the cell-like room with only a mattress on the floor is the lowest point of my life. Her arms and neck are thin and white under the bandages; her baseball hat covers her face. She doesn't come to the window when we call. I've never felt more hopeless. I can't even comfort Lars.

At home, Lars and I slump on the couch. "Let's get all her stuff from her room and give it away," he says and his eyes are wild.

"Why?" I don't see what he means.

"Cause she's not going to make it."

When I said goodbye to Joanie, after cleaning her home and doing some ironing she said, " Thank you very much, you are a good kid and I hope you will have a nice trip." I somewhat want to see her when I am back, but she does not look happy and well, so maybe it would be the best if she just starts her own trip before I came back.

That night my two sleeping pills don't work at all. I just lie there; I'm too tired to read. And if I couldn't sleep, I wonder how Ellie felt in her locked cell with what little she has to look forward to.

I get to the office with desperate determination to do something. I know I can't care for Ellie at home. I've brought my old insurance papers, and I dig them out of my purse. With trembling hands, I call my ex's insurance company and ask to speak to someone about my daughter's file. I don't have a real plan in mind but I'm desperate enough to try anything.

"This is Mrs. Jensen," I announce, squeezing the phone, gambling that this person won't know I haven't been Mrs. for five years. "What is holding up the approval for the Head Injury Recovery Center in Berkeley for my daughter, Ellie Jensen? I'm told there's some kind of delay. "

"We have approved all expenses—therapy, treatments, ongoing care, etc. Except for room and board. That's all we can pay. Mr. Jensen insists that we pay it all."

"We've changed our minds on that," I say hurriedly, "we'll pay room and board ourselves. Can we have a letter going to the BAHIRC confirming that you'll pay the $8000 a month for her care?"

"Yes, we can send that out."

"Good, and a copy for us, please."

I am breathing hard. I quickly look up the number for the BAHIRC and ask to talk to Dr. Gregory.

"I just talked to the insurance company. They will pay all expenses for Ellie except room and board. Is it still $2000 a month? I'll find a way to pay it."

"We'll take her for the $8000 and waive the fee for the room and board."
They don't know yet about her suicide try. I hope it's not too late.

Subject: home again
Date: Sept. 1, 1998

I was the walking dead at the gym at 4:00 AM this morning but, it
always feels good after a workout! It only took a few days to sleep
beyond 4AM when I was in Oregon with Lars and Josie. I think Josie
still may be a little mad at me for the time I tried to die by cutting
my wrists.

Ellie is still at the lock-up facility. When I visit the day room, one patient
is dusting the tables and chairs. "I'm getting ready for a party," she says.

"Okay," I say, "good work."

"You can wear my diamond ring," another patient says, "I only trust you
and Jesus."

Ellie and I stand in a corner. She says, "I'm not crazy, Mom. Can I go?"

"Yes," I say. "We're breaking you out soon. Here," I tuck a bundle in her
jacket. "I smuggled in your radio."

The next day at lunchtime I pick up Ellie from the facility and take her to
the Hof Brau where they have the best Chinese food in Merced. We have the BBQ
pork and noodles. "The arrangements for Berkeley are almost done," I tell her, "but
they are concerned about the suicide try. I'm asking Dave and Jemma to call them
with assurances that it was only a suicide 'gesture.'"

"I'm sorry, Mom. I hate it here."

"I know. It's hard to wait. It seems like it was taking forever to get the
insurance okay." I hug her thin body. "You'll do better once you get to Berkeley. "

"I'm sorry—my—" She gestures to the back of her head as if she's pulling
her hair.

"Your braid?," I ask. "Where is it?"

"I— burned—it. I wanted it to go before me."

Subject: Books on tape
Date: Sept. 4, 1998

I didn't get my library tapes back in time and now the library lady is mad with me. But I did finally get that book BLACK HOLES AND TIME WARPS: EINSTEIN'S OUTRAGEOUS LEGACY. I hope I can understand it with my new brain.

Ellie is discharged from the mental facility to a halfway house until preparations for Berkeley are complete. The halfway house is dingy, old and in a rural area of Merced. The added-on bedrooms ramble toward the rear of the house through a long, dark hall.

Ellie's room has fake wood paneling, a single bed and a desk. Deep cigarette burns mar the counters in the kitchen and a strong odor of stale smoke and 409 cleaning solution stings my nose. I don't dare to look in the bathroom. I just want to get her out of here before depression overcomes her again.

When I'm visiting, I talk with the other patients. They seem to be almost as disturbed as the ones in the lock-up. One young man with thick glasses, Charles, is very friendly. "Ellie, can we take the bus to the mall? They have French fries."

"Maybe," Ellie says.

Charles hangs around whenever I'm there. He seems to have a crush on Ellie. I can see why; she looks attractive despite her short hair, which is growing out in a pixie cut like she wore as a child. She is thin but her shape under baggy jeans and t-shirts is feminine. Now I have a new worry. She'll attract men, but what kind? And how will she react?

Subject: new clothes
Date: Sept. 10, 1998

I have been wearing my new shirt & white overalls!! It is very nice to have some new clothes. I meet my friend Lisa in Cimarron when I was 18. She is one of my oldest friends, and I am very happy we still write to each other. I started to listen to Lord Jim by Joseph Conrad on Saturday. It is sad and somewhat uncomfortable:

because Jim is such a loser, and it is uncomfortable because I have used some of Jim's rationales in the past. I want to shake Jim and tell him to wise up!

10

Berkeley on Contract

Judy and I drive Ellie to Berkeley on April 12th. I'm surprised she leaves her big teddy bear—the one she clutched on the plane ride from Farmington and slept with every night. She takes only a small duffel bag. It's another sparkling day and a cool wind sweeps over from the blue bay.

The BAHIRC is located on Woolsey Avenue not far from the Berkeley campus. On Telegraph Avenue the street vendors are out with their jewelry and other wares. I love the cool ocean breeze after the valley heat.

The two-story house has brown shingles and a small front yard with untrimmed bushes. Inside, the rooms have a cluttered, lived-in look. I smell spaghetti sauce cooking. Ellie's room is on the ground floor, with high ceilings, a view of the backyard and a private bath. Marti, the friendly counselor that we met on our previous visit, greets us and we all help Ellie unpack. I take pictures of Ellie and Judy on the porch and of Ellie and Marti wearing the joke glasses.

Ellie is the only female out of the twelve residents at the facility. After I meet the other residents, I think she is probably the highest functioning, for which I suddenly feel grateful. I wonder at the history of the other patients—were they injured in cars or motorcycles or were they victims of violent crime like Ellie?

"Ellie, can I see you and your mother in my office?" Dr. Gregory is on hand to welcome her.

"As a condition of your acceptance at this facility, Ellie, we need you to sign a contract that you will not hurt yourself."

"Ellie?" I say.

"Let's make it for one month." Dr. Gregory hands the paper to her.

"Read," Ellie gestures toward me.

"I, Ellie Jensen, agree to not run away, or try to hurt myself while at the Bay Area Head Injury Center. This contract is good for 30 days and renewable for each month I spend here. "

She shakes her head. "A month is a long time."

"What about one week then? Seven days?" Dr. Gregory asks. "Renewed every week."

"Okay. Okay for me." She curls her hand around the pen in her curious left-handed fashion and prints Else Ane Jensen on the contract.

Subj: love
Date: Sept. 14, 1998

When I cam home there was a letter for me from my good friend Lisa. She is in love and some of her happiness had dripped down her arm to her hand and into my letter! I guess I wish love would come back to me! I'm planning to wear my new white overalls to the movie today.

Ellie's settled in Berkeley. I'm breathing a little easier when the public prosecutor in Cimarron calls. "We're preparing to try Frank Harmon. Can Ellie come for the trial? Or if she can't, can you make the trip?" I picture a boyish guy wearing rumpled khaki slacks, a white polyester shirt and a narrow tie. His youthful voice makes me feel ancient.

"Uh—I don't know. She's just starting a residential recovery program."

"What's her condition?" He asks.

"As you probably know her skull was broken in several places. Cracked liked an eggshell. She was in coma for nearly a month. She has recovered some speech and most of her physical capabilities but she's significantly impaired in cognitive, memory and reasoning. She'll need another surgery to repair the bone loss in her head."

"Awful, just awful. Nobody here has any sympathy for him. They're pulling for her. But he has to be tried. It would help my case if a family member testified. I'd like to get a first-degree attempted murder conviction."

"Can't I just send the medical reports? I've already taken a great deal of time off work but the main thing is I need to be here with Ellie. Also, I don't know if I could face him. Harmon, that is."

"I understand. He's confessed to attacking her, of course."

"Did he say why?"

"He said something about Ellie tossing a soda can at him."

"Ridiculous! Ellie doesn't even drink soda!"

"That's what I heard. Also the owner of the radio station said soda wasn't allowed in the control room. Nobody here believes him or can imagine why he did such a thing. There was some talk about moving the trial but the county can't afford it. He has a public defender, also."

"A public prosecutor and public defender? What kind of a trial is that?"

"He has no funds to hire anyone."

"Do you think I care about that? Or him?" There's an uncomfortable silence on the line.

"What about Ellie's father? Maybe he'd be willing to testify."

"I doubt it. You could check with him. Do you have his phone number?"

"Yes. Can you let me know as soon as possible? The trial is scheduled in three weeks. It will take about a week."

"Okay. I'll talk to Ellie."

"Thank you Mrs. Jensen. And good luck with the rehab."

"What do you want to do? About the trial. The public prosecutor wants me to go." Ellie and I are sitting on her bed in Berkeley.

"I don't see him. I'm not strong anymore." She turns her face to the wall.

I rub her back between her thin shoulders. "You don't need to go. You're making good progress here." She nods her head. I notice that she isn't wearing the army cap pulled low over her eyes. Instead she has a small white knitted cap more like a yarmulke. "What do you want me to do? Should I go testify?"

"No. He might hurt you."

"I'm not worried—the little coward is locked up. I think they have plenty of evidence without us. I'll send the hospital and doctor reports. Or your Dad?" I ask. "Maybe he'll go."

"Dad tell me he'll kill him."

"I'd help him do that. But then we'd both go to prison and what good would that do? We want to be here to help you."

"Am I better? I didn't protect from him."

"A lot better! Your speech is really improving. Look how you can get around Berkeley all by yourself."

Driving home, I ponder the situation. Maybe I should go. I think of sitting in a courtroom, watching Frank Harmon shuffle in, his legs and arms shackled. I realize I don't know what he looks like. And I don't want to know. I don't want anything of his voice, face, or appearance to be in my mind. I just can't afford the emotion.

Gary declines to go to the trial also. The prosecutor sounds disappointed when he calls me. "The trial was only four days. Harmon got 2nd degree attempted murder. That was the best I could do."

"Was it a plea bargain?" I picture a meeting at a coffee shop where the defending attorney writes a number on a paper napkin and slides it across the table. Like negotiating for a new car. "What about the sentence? Ellie's still afraid of him."

"I'm hoping for a long sentence. Apparently, he's afraid of prison, worried that he'll be molested."

"Is that likely to happen?" I feel disgusted.

"Let me put it this way—his type of crime won't be looked on kindly by the other inmates. Attacking a young girl."

"I'm not sympathetic. Let his mother worry about that."

"I understand how you feel. I'll keep you updated."

Subj: Another foggy morning
Sept. 17, 1998

I went out bicycling on Sat. & Sun. I have been enjoying Lord Jim, but much of the point of view and the narrative is from an older sea captain So I am somewhat irritated because of his racist attitude, but it is a good book I call rehab last week but my counselor was out for a few weeks. My problem with AOL was cleared up when I stop using AOL. Enjoy the sun in Sac, we have not seen it that much here.

11

Stay in the Present

The house seems empty after visiting Ellie in Berkeley. I remove the paper bag with the knives from the trunk of the car. I dump them into the kitchen drawer.

Before work, I climb on the ladder and polish the outside of Ellie's bedroom window with Windex and newspapers. Cleaning sure beats spying. I vacuum furiously in Ellie's bedroom and dust the closet shelves. Her teddy bear watches me from her bed, his head leaning slightly. I straighten him up and see that his throat is cut. Inside his body Ellie has stored a supply of pills—the phenabarbs that she was supposed to take for anti-seizure medication. Abruptly, I perch on the side of her waterbed. I'm overcome with relief. I'm betting that she stored them up for her suicide try and then, because of her short-term memory loss forgot where she put them.

That night, my friend Annetta invites me out for a glass of wine after work. I sink into the deep green booth at Mallards. It's a restaurant/bar and a hangout for singles. The air conditioning blows on my bare arms. I'm chilly—goose bumps spread up my arms. But I welcome any feeling in my body—four months after the attack on Ellie, it's as if I'm just coming out of shock. I slip off my sandals and put my feet up beside Annetta.

"Two chardonnays, two glasses of water with lemon." Annetta doesn't need to consult me.

"How're things? Is Ellie settling in?"

"Yes, it's kind of a miracle. She takes the bus every day to the speech therapist. She even wrote me a letter. But, people have stopped asking about her. They look at me like I'm the one who's disabled."

"They care," Annetta reassures me, "they just don't know what to say."

"Hmm."

"Are you missing her?"

"Do you know what it's like to be on suicide watch?" I shudder. "I was almost relieved when it happened."

"Are you sleeping?"

"Don't say I look tired."

"You look relaxed—more so than usual."

"I have this stress test I do. I look in the mirror, relax my mouth and if my lower lip doesn't tremble, I'm okay. Like this." I demonstrate.

We laugh and a man sitting at the bar glances over.

"He's cute, Annetta. Cross your legs, toss your hair or something."

"He's probably married or an alcoholic—that's his third beer—but who's counting. By the way, how's Andy?"

"He's busy as ever but drives me up to see Ellie. Takes us out for meals. And he treats her—well, like a normal person."

"That's good to hear. He's really coming through for you." I take the last sip of wine, surprised by the lingering fruity taste. I realize I'm wrong about ever enjoying anything again.

"Want another glass?" Annetta asks.

"No, I feel perfect right now. I have a new system. I don't think about what happened or try to figure out the future. I stay in the present. It's hard for anything to hurt me when I'm in the present."

Subj: Sunny Day
Date: Sept. 22, 1998

Yes, Joanie is till hanging on. Lord Jim was a good read but I have been enjoying Dr. Zhivago a bit more. I get another book by Joseph Conrad (he wrote Lord Jim) at the tape library last week. It is called Nostomo and is mentioned as his greatest novel. I got the tape of Madam Bovary and started yesterday, I am so happy I have been born now than in the 18 century in Normandy! I hope Andy's finger is feeling better after that spider bite.

After work, about 5:30, I sit on my bed to read Ellie's intake assessment from the BAHIRC that I received in the mail today. The envelope is thick and cream-colored with my address printed in blue ink. I hold it in my hand a long time before I can open it. The sprinkler is going on the back lawn and a fine mist filters in through the open sliding glass door. Fellini, our big black cat, keeps me company. He purrs on my lap, making bread with his claws, moving gently in and out on my bare legs.

I speed read the first page, noting phrases: reading problems, difficulty writing at a single word level, verbal and non-verbal comprehension and reasoning abilities are severely impaired, processing speed profoundly slowed, simple sequencing was very difficult and complex sequencing seemingly impossible, problems revolving around anxiety, depression and withdrawal. I jump to page three where I quickly read more, with my heart sinking:

COGNITIVE ASSESSMENT RATING SCORE:
(Scores converted to a 0-6 functional disability scale)

  0 = no disability
1-2 = mild disability
     (indicates at least 1 below the normal range of function)
3-4 = moderate disability
     (indicates at least 2 below the normal range of function)
5-6 = maximum disability
     (indicates at least 3 below the normal range of function)

She has fives in word finding, syntax, contextual thinking, planning, organization decision making, self-esteem and self-worth.

I turn the page and read the interviews:

Else Ane was cooperative, pleasant, and able to make her ideas known. She is single and apparently has always been a rather independent individual. According to available records, her mother describes her as being likable, friendly and bright. She passed her GED requirement in her sophomore year. In Cimarron, Colo. she was working as a disc jockey at a local radio station. She does have rather severe expressive aphasia difficulties. Two interviews were conducted; one while her mother was here and then when accompanied by her father. They apparently are separated or divorced at this time. Her father reports that she does not know how to apply makeup at this time. Else Ane reports that in the past she has always liked to read but now finds that difficult. She does not know the letters of the alphabet at this time. Measures of cognitive function were attempted with Else Ane being reluctant to complete these. She seems to have a fear of failure and of looking bad. She was able to complete the Trail Making A Test within 73 seconds. This is approximately twice as long as would be expected for someone her age. She was very reluctant to complete the Trail Making B Test and thus this measure was not able to be administered. During the course of the interviews, Else Ane was noted to be rather severely depressed. She reported being afraid now to make friends or develop friendships. She reports feeling sometimes wanting "to die" or "to run away." It was pointed out to her that monthly contracts would have to be made with her stating that she would agree not to attempt suicide or run away while attending this program. She was very reluctant to contract for the period of a month stating that was a very long time. Due to her recent suicide gesture, a weekly contract will be made with her. It is important to note that her father during one of the intake interviews stated that if anything happened to his daughter he would "sue our asses off." This was stated in a half-joking manner but the intent was apparently quite serious. Thus, the contract will be very strictly adhered to or else Else Ane will be terminated from the program. If Else Ane does agree to the weekly signing of a contract, then we will be delighted to consider her as a candidate for the BAHIRC.

I drop the assessment, dump Fellini out of my lap, and rush outside. I grab the hedge trimmers and attack the mock orange bushes. I whack off the new growth as the words from the report whirl in my head: self-esteem, lawsuits, divorce, suicide gestures, severe aphasia, trail making, impairment—makeup.

———————

Subj: no overnight
Sept. 28, 1998

They have been logging the trees at the Moose Loyal Order by my house for a week or so, it is really sad Joanie looks about the same, last week she wanted me to stay at night for a few days a week. I told her I am not sure and need to talk with Debbie at the hospice. I did not call Deb because it is hard to say no to a dying person. But Deb at the Hospice called Kate (Joanie's mom) and told her she needs to pay $ to someone to stay overnight and a hospice vol. cannot be used that way. Deb saved me from saying no to Joanie. You were right about Madam Bovary, very grim Madame Bovary was in a higher class than most but there was not much of a life as a women at that time.

"Mac-ro-bi-ot-ic," I say, dividing the word in syllables.
"M," Ellie prints on her paper, but looks at me for the next letter.

We are sitting on the rocks on Skyline Blvd. above Berkeley. Below us are Oakland, the Bay and the Golden Gate Bridge. The air is a misty blue with an acrid smell of eucalyptus. I remember the year of the deep frost that killed a huge number of the eucalyptus trees in the area. At the time I was attending Mills College and commuted from Merced several times a week. The trees looked so sad with their dry, dead leaves.

I'm drilling Ellie on her spelling from small index cards she brings along wherever we go. The BAHIRC has turned her around—she has regained her independence by taking the bus all over Berkeley to her therapy appointments, she's wowing the house when it's her turn to cook, has made friends with some of the other patients. She still has to renew her weekly contract agreeing not to hurt herself.

I give her the next word. "Tu-mul-tu-ous,"

She prints carefully, her left hand curved around the pencil.

"I knew you were going to be left-handed when you were four months old. You held your rattle in your left hand and grabbed your bottle with the left hand, too." She doesn't look up but smiles. Her right side paralysis has mostly resolved and her smile is straight.

"Why do you pick such hard words?" I ask.

"Mom," her thin face is earnest, "I want to learn." Ellie's hair sticks out from the knitted cap at a funny angle. There is still a large depression on the right side of her skull. When I smooth her hair, I feel the ridges and bumps.

Subj: will
Date: Sept. 30, 1998

I just came home from the post office. THANKS for the money! At end of this month, extra cash is very nice! I have copied my will and thought I would send a copy to you for save keeping. I need to clean the house today but will wait until Keith wakes up. We are broken up as a romance and he doesn't want to be just friends.

12

New Earrings

Today, May 28, Ellie's nineteen and in Merced for her birthday party.

"Who comes?" Ellie asks, then corrects herself, "who is coming?"

"Andy, Blake, of course, Karen and a bunch of my friends, Jemma and her husband, the group from The Soup Kitchen. Most of your friends are still at college, Josie and Lars are in Colorado."

Ellie sits on my bed with the cat on her lap. "What should I wear?" I ponder the closet selection. "Maybe this sundress I got in Berkeley." I slip the blue dress over my head. Ellie points to my bra straps. "I'll take it off." I slip the bra off—I've lost so much weight I don't really need it.

"What are you wearing?"

Ellie points to her long sleeve button-down shirt.

"It's too hot; what else do you have?"

"This." She tugs her sleeves down over her scarred wrists and buttons her top button. Her neck cut is almost healed; luckily, she missed her jugular.

The people pour in through the back gate. Jemma, the speech therapist, brings her husband, Nick, whom I haven't met before. He seems to match her in niceness. Marti and husband Dave (who work in the restaurant where Ellie was employed) bring their boys eight and ten and two of the boys' friends. The kids run around the back yard trying to play with Fellini who hides under the photinia bushes. Then Judy arrives with her dogs, Wally and Lady. The yard is full of barking dogs and laughing, yelling boys.

Everybody has brought a dish and the picnic table is loaded with fruit, potato and pasta salads, quiches, brownies, watermelon and a carrot cake studded with pecans and smothered with cream cheese frosting—Ellie's favorite cake. I've set out coolers with beer and soft drinks and decorated the picnic table with balloons and flowers. I light the coals in the Weber and we grill chicken and hot dogs for the kids.

Marti talks about the trip they are planning to Guatemala. They will manage a restaurant down there for about a year. Marti and Ellie have been working out new recipes for the Guatemalan restaurant. Marti suggests that Ellie go with them to Guatemala for at least part of the time. An interesting idea, but Ellie wants to stay in Berkeley for now.

I've got the camera clicking all afternoon. Ellie looks like a pixie—her hair is just long enough to cover the scars on her head. We sing "Happy Birthday." She tips her head and smiles—her new silver and turquoise earrings (from the gift shop in Gallup) flashing in the sunlight. I feel a lavish sweep of happiness.

Subj: not better
Date: October 1, 1998

School started on Tuesday, I am taking a ET 10, which is a intro into electronics and its lab. I will see how it will go. The text book and the lab book were too much money so I copied the whole lab book which cost 10$ then returned the lab book at the book store. It was a pain to copy the whole book but I saved 20$. Joanie looked much better on Monday than the week before. I am having some problems with Keith now, we have got more friendly lately and he has been touching me now and again and a few times he has tried to kiss me. We really need to talk about this but he gets so mad and surly, I have been waiting until it needs to be talk about and I hope it will just go away but I know it will not get better without some help.

13

Repairing

"Let's use Cherry Blossoms in the Snow," I hold out the bottle of nail polish. "I haven't done my nails for months." This weekend is the annual October get-together with my women friends at Pajaro Dunes in Monterey. We five: Sally, Sunny, Debbie, Dr. Debbie and I are friends who met in graduate school at Mills College. It's the first weekend I haven't seen Ellie since she left for Berkeley. I lie on the deck of our rented condo in my yellow swimsuit. The weathered boards are hard against my stomach. I'm warm all over, even my toes. Above me a red kite hangs in the cool ocean air.

"Should my nail polish match the color on my toes?" Sally asks.

"No. Unless you have someone to rub your feet," Debbie answers.

"Remember we've banned talking about men all weekend," I say. And I've already given them an update on Ellie, so that's over.

"Well, a woman could rub your feet." Alison's the practical one.

"I suppose," I say.

"Yes," Dr. Debbie instructs us. "And then you wouldn't have to show your gratitude."

"New subject," Sally announces.

"What new subject?" Debbie asks. "How about waiting until lunch?" She bustles to the kitchen and opens and closes things. She comes back carrying a tray with a sour dough baguette, sliced salami, pepperoncini and a jar of Best Foods mayonnaise. Dr. Debbie has produced a bottle of cold wine and five glasses.

"Be careful of your polish," Sunny cautions.

"Andrea's engaged."

"But Sally, she's only twenty." Debbie says.

"Well, I can't wait to be the mother of the bride. And," Sally takes a slug of wine, " I'm getting her a Vera Wang gown."

"What's that going to run you?" Alison asks.

"Listen to this. I went to a showing of her gowns. No cameras were allowed.

But I took a small sketchpad and slipped it out of my purse. I'm having the dress made for $500 instead of $4000."

"What's it like?" Alison asks.

"Beautiful—a fitted top, a full skirt with tulle pastel layers. Like the memory of a rainbow."

"I'm giving the shower," Dr. Debbie says. "You're all invited."

Later, after two coats of polish, we take pictures of our hands fanned in a circle. I recognize my hand when I develop the pictures; it's the thinnest and most wrinkled.

Subj: afraid
Date: October 3, 1998

I just came home from Joanie's apt. The hospice called this morning and said that she may not make it beyond today, so I was with her for about 6 hours today. It is a very sad day today for me and her family. Joanie is afraid of dying (like all of us!), and I wanted to take away the fear from her and give her peace, but how can I do that? Life can be so sad sometimes,

November 11, 1988

"The short hair cut again?" Ellie looks in the mirror and ruffles her hair, which has grown back to rich brown bangs and medium length. It's November 11th and she is back in Merced for surgery to repair the depression in the left side of her skull.

"Actually," I correct her, "they'll shave it."

"I know."

I walk down the hall by her gurney. I kiss her good-bye. "See you in the recovery room."

Another hospital. Gary and I sit on opposite sides of the waiting room. The surgery will take about two hours. It's as if someone opened up a can of hospital smell from Farmington: Gary's cologne, floor wax, disinfectant, stale smoke and burned coffee. He's reading *Time Magazine* and swinging his leg back and forth, back and forth. I remember in our early marriage years how the weekly arrival of

Time was an event. We both wanted to be the first reader. Once we fought and ripped it. That mistake resolved the problem. Upon arrival, we'd tear it in half, read our half and exchange.

"Gary?"

"What?"

"Can I have half?"

He holds it out and pretends to rip it. We laugh together.

Later, Gary and I watch Ellie from the recovery room window. Her skin is paler than skim milk and her head is heavily bandaged.

"Wouldn't it be great if they could've repaired her speech and cognitive problems as easily as they can patch and round out her skull?" I hold his gaze like I haven't done for a long time.

"Yes." Gary chokes up.

We stand side by side, our shoulders touching, looking through the window into the recovery room at our daughter. Neither of us tries to move away.

The doctor, in his scrubs, enters the recovery room by the side door, beckons to us, "You can come in now. Everything went well."

We both begin breathing again.

Subj: Cloudy Day
Date: October 11, 1998

It looks and smells that summer is turning into fall here; it seems that summer was too short! Hospice called on Tuesday to say that Joanie died on yesterday at 5 pm. I will take a week off before I start up being a Hospice vol. Again. I'm reading 'Seeds of Change; five plants that transformed mankind.'

"What about the radio station? Did they have insurance?" I'm talking to Ellie's attorney, Carl, in Colorado.

"Yes, they had liability insurance but it lapsed for non-payment. Then the night of the attack they slipped their payment under the door of the agency. However, she left the station door unlocked so they would claim contributory negligence."

"But everyone left the door unlocked."

"It was a regulation even if everyone ignored it."

"What about workmen's comp?"

"That fell through, also. Since Ellie knew her attacker they claim it wasn't work related."

"Knew him? Everyone in town knew everyone—that doesn't seem fair."

"I know. But there's no point in pursuing that avenue."

"I trust your judgment on all the legal things. So what's next?"

"I flew to Durango to interview the psychiatrist that was treating Frank Harmon. He can't testify because of doctor/patient confidentiality."

"Did he know Harmon was obsessed with Ellie? For God's sake, why didn't he warn her?"

"It's hard to know just what went on in their sessions. Apparently, Harmon had mentioned that he wanted her to be his girl friend."

"How could he not know Harmon was dangerous? It's so frustrating."

"I wish I could have good news. I just can't be optimistic about recovering anything for her medical costs."

"What am I going to do with the bills from the doctors and hospitals in Durango and Farmington?"

"Forward them to me for now."

"I can't believe Ellie will get nothing for what she's suffered. What kind of a future will she have if she has to rely on social security?"

Subj: More Clouds
Date: October 15, 1998

When I woke up this morning I thought it was Sat. And it took me 45 min and 2 miles bike riding before it came to me it was Friday! When I was talking with the Hospice this morning, they gave me a new phone number so I could start work with someone new, there was no one home when I called and I think I may wait until tomorrow because I am somewhat sadded by Joanie's death.

It's our first holiday, Thanksgiving, since Ellie's accident. Grandma Max and Grandpa Hal, my parents, drive out from Washington and join me, Lars, Josie and Andy in a rented cabin near Arnold, California on Hwy 4. We have the turkey, the ski clothes, the extra TV.

"Let's not ski today, it's snowing too hard," I suggest.

"I'm going," Lars says.

"I'm not." Josie is firm.

"Good," I say. "Let's get Mom to make rolls."

"I want—to learn the—" Ellie gestures with her left hand.

"The recipe," Josie furnishes the word, "me, too."

My Mom has been making huge batches of yeast rolls for years. At Christmas the plastic wrapped packages were lined up on the counter waiting for my Dad to deliver to the neighbors. Sometimes he'd be gone for hours—back just in time but smelling of whiskey for our Christmas Eve church program. Because the recipe seemed so complicated and took so much time, none of her four daughters (including me) have learned the method. Besides, when Mom came to visit she always left plenty of her special rolls in the freezer.

"What kind?" Mom washes her hands.

"Cinnamon, caramel and horners."

"Yes, butter horns with lemon butter frosting," Josie adds.

"Start with nine or ten cups of flour," Mom begins, "then—"

"Not so fast," Josie says. "Wait until I can get something to write with."

We work together, measuring and mixing. While the dough is rising on the counter in large bowls covered with dishtowels, Andy gets his guitar. On a kitchen stool he swivels toward me and strums and then sings in a heart-breaking tenor—a croon that would cause Danny Boy to rise from the grave and dance with his mother.

"Softly, tenderly, Jesus is Calling, Calling for you and for me." His wine dark eyes draw me in. Although it's a hymn, I'm being seduced and it feels good.

The rolls turn out high, light and delicious. The dough is melty tender, the butter melts and I melt. It is warm and steamy in the cabin and snowy outside and I'd like this close family time to last forever.

Later, Ellie wants to go out. I'm surprised by her sudden request.

"It's dark, snowy—you can't walk anywhere." I try to reason with her. She gets mad and storms out the door. As the head injury book predicts, she is unable to control her emotions. The panic I seem to carry in reserve grabs me and I drive around looking for her. The snowy roads are empty. We eat dinner with our eyes on the door. After dark she strolls in, and seems to have left her mad somewhere. I go from fear to relief in three seconds and hug her tightly. She looks relieved to be back inside.

Subj: too much water
Date: October 19, 1998

I just came home from an ultrasound of my ovarys. They made you drink 40 oz. Of water then wait for 1 1/2 hours without going to the bathroom. My bladder was not happy but the ultrasound did not hurt. Have you done this before?

Keith did not take the microwave but he did take the vacuum cleaner. Can I have your old one if you still have it?

14

Soul

December 9, 1988

"Ellie? How are you doing?" I call her in Berkeley. Before each call I prepare myself mentally for the Ellie with the hesitant speech. Even though I've prepared, a little baptism of sadness always washes over me.

"This is it—what's the word?"

"Anniversary. A year ago today."

"Long, long time."

"I heard from the court—2nd degree attempted murder. Fourteen years in prison."

"Not enough."

"I know. But the important thing is your progress. Carl said he'd probably have a rough time in prison. May be assaulted by the other inmates."

"Don't care. Hate him. I get bad dreams every night." Ellie hangs up on me.

Last weekend Andy and I took Ellie to Golden Gate Park in San Francisco. Going into the planetarium, we lost her temporarily. I searched around frantically and found her with an old woman who was separated from her son. The woman was obviously mentally ill but Ellie tried to calm her and even invited her to spend the day with us and go home with us if we can't find her son. Will there be a problem with her being overly compassionate?

Tonight my friends are getting together to rent the Jack Nicholson movie, "The Shining," but I'll pass because I can't bring myself to see movies with such violence; it's too real for me. Besides an aversion to movie violence, I break into tears at odd moments. My crying is like aftershocks from the large magnitude earthquake. Some shocks are a small jolt like when I hear the Cat Stevens song, "Moon Shadow," that Ellie used to like. I used to tease her that one of her first boyfriends looked like Cat Stevens. For this memory my tears are the quiet, leaking kind. Today I had a huge aftershock when I saw the fall display of lunchboxes at Payless. In the fall both Lars and Ellie would spend hours deciding which action hero or TV character they wanted on their lunchbox. This aftershock resulted in a sobbing breakdown in the checkout line. A man buying mouthwash glances away but the young woman behind me pats my back.

Subj: More medical stuff
Date: November 3, 1998

The check should be written to Humboldt Open Door Dental Clinic for $430. I think you would need to write a note with the check saying the money is for Ellie's new crown.

Ellie is home for Christmas. I remember our Christmas last year when she was still in coma and I was at the Swenson's in Denver. I remember their kindness and want to buy them a special gift. At an Oakdale church, which sells native crafts from around the world, I find a carved wood Nativity set. Jesus and Mary were given lodging by strangers at a crucial time, as I did.

The highlight for me, this year, is when we all attend a Christmas Eve church service. At the end of the service, with lights out, we hold candles, which we light, one to the next, down the rows, until the sanctuary is glowing with candlelight.

"Peace be with you," I say holding my candle with one hand and my other arm around Ellie.

She's holding her own candle and repeats carefully, "Peace with you," and lights the next candle.

Later we sit by the light of the Christmas tree. "What's this?" Ellie unwraps a gift.

"Harmonica. You can learn to play that," I say, "because music is like math and your math skills are good."

"The man—?" Ellie can't say his name.

"Leon Redbone," Lars supplies. "He has soul. You need that to play the harmonica."

"Do I have soul?" she asks.

"Oh my God." I hug her tightly. "You have more soul than the all the rest of us put together!"

"I do? Then I can play the harmonica, too."

However, Ellie's attempt to play ends in frustration. I hear some sour notes from her room.

"Let's go," she says only two days after Christmas.

"Are you in a rush? Do you want to start your classes?"

"To see my scribes."

She has been taking some remedial classes at Laney Jr. College in Oakland. Our California college system provides her with free tutors to help her write papers, take tests and read her textbooks on tapes. Then she can listen slowly and replay passages over if she needs to.

We make the familiar drive back to Berkeley. Her tape player sits on her desk. The house is quiet—the others aren't back yet. I fluff the pillows on her bed.

"Do you want to come back home when you're finished here?"

"No." She puts her bag in the closet.

"Why?"

"It's okay to be weird in Berkeley."

She leaves her harmonica at home in her room.

Subj: Holidays
Date: November 26, 1998

Good to talk with you and Andy on Thanksgiving. I took a real long bike ride and thought about how glad I am not to be trapped in a wheelchair. Do you think I really would have run away from the hospital in San Jose if they didn't put that long stick on my wheelchair so I couldn't get out the doors?

15

Independence

February 8, 1989

"They told me they were done with me." Ellie says on the phone. She's ready to leave the BAHIRC for more study at Santa Rosa Junior College.

"So soon? It seems too soon. Do you want me to drive you?"

"No. I'm bussing to that town."

"Forestville?" I ask.

"Yes, that's it. I can't tell the name sometimes."

I'm apprehensive but remember my plan to encourage her independence. "Okay. Call me as soon as you get there."

The next day I get an envelope in the mail from her. It contains a money order for sixty-five dollars and a printed note on yellow-lined notebook paper. The note is folded small and I carefully unwrap it. "This is to pay you back for the money you loaned me to take the bus trip to Cimarron. Love, Ellie."

I feel another wave of sadness when I see her careful printing and remember she can't write cursive anymore. I consider sending the money back, as she needs it more than I do. But I don't want to jeopardize her hard-won independence. This freedom is what she's been working toward for a year and a half. I feel like I did on her first day of school when she walked away from me toward her classroom—a small girl in a corduroy jumper that I stitched up myself leaving her mother and babyhood behind.

Subj: deer
Date: December 1, 1998

Thanks for the coffee. The rain has end and the roads are drying out. I have been watching our three deer and studying the French Revolution.

Although the lawsuits on Ellie's behalf fall through, her application for social security and disability is approved. I first filed on her behalf when she was still in coma. This application was turned down; the reply stated, "She would be able to find work." I filed a second time, and she was declared ineligible because of possible future jobs as an envelope stuffer or collator. I've gotten an education on the availability of medical services and social security payments for the disabled.

Before the third try, I consulted a lawyer who specializes in social security claims. "Almost all applications are turned down at least twice. A judge only approves some after three denials. This is the President's idea of cutting the budget," the lawyer informs me.

I check out a thick book from the library on Social Security law. This time I word the application precisely with the language they want to hear and I back up the application with the medical reports that I personally request from the attending doctors.

Ellie's social security and disability benefits amount to about $600 a month. Also she has about $1500 in the bank of accrued benefits. I am her payee and will keep the financial records. Her benefits are subject to review at least once a year.

I hope that having some money of her own will help Ellie win back a degree of independence.

Subject:no tlak
Date: December 10, 1998

My hospice person was awake some of the time today but she does not like to talk at all. Her son had given her some chocolate so I fed her some.

Yes, I miss Keith some but we just couldn't make it. It'll do better after awhile.

16

The Psychic

April 20, 1989

"Can you go with me on Saturday?" Annetta invites me to Stockton.

"What do you have in mind?"

"It's a secret."

"Give me a hint. I need something to look forward to."

"It might help Ellie."

It is a soft, spring day in the Central Valley. We speed along Highway 99 through almond and walnut orchards. Beside us, the irrigation canals glitter like long mirrors.

In route, she discloses our destination. "We're going to consult with a psychic healer."

"Pretty weird."

"I know." Annetta smiles. "But let's see what we can get out of a session."

"What are you going to work on?" I ask. Annetta is a psychologist and I respect her opinions.

"I won't know until I get started."

A woman greets us at the door of a suburban tract house. She's leggy and tan with smooth blonde hair. "I'm Carla." She leads us through her well-decorated house to the backyard pool. We stop near a man sleeping in a lounge chair. "That's Scott, my husband. He's on an astral journey."

Annetta goes in the house to consult the psychic first. I wait outside by the pool. The pool sweep hisses and I slide off my shoes and stretch my feet and legs in the sun. I wish I had my suit. There is a faint smell of chlorine and a strong fragrance from the star jasmine climbing the fence.

Annetta is gone for a long time. When she comes out her blue eyes are clearer than ever and her skin seems to glow.

"Your turn." Annetta smiles like she knows a secret. I feel like I'm going for an audience with the pope.

In the living room the psychic is standing in front of a large easel covered with blank paper. On the easel ledge are different colored flow pens. The psychic is about sixty, wearing brown trousers and a tan shirt under a shapeless gray cardigan. His face is pear-shaped. His eyes droop and remind me of those of my long dead cocker spaniel, Tipper.

"I'm Barbara Jensen. I'm here to see if I can help my daughter."

"I'm Clifton Murch." He holds out a large, meaty hand and we shake. "Why don't you sit?" He gestures to a chair by the easel. "And what's her name?"

"Else Ane." Now, I think he looks a little like my Grandfather, Raymond Johnson, on my mother's side.

"Tell me about your daughter," the psychic asks.

I plunge into her story. "A year ago when she was eighteen she went to work in Cimarron, Colorado for the summer. She stayed on in the fall with two jobs: cook in restaurant and as an announcer at a small, local radio station. There was a young man who was a former employee of the small radio station. He had been fired from his job but still hung around the radio station. Apparently, he had some emotional problems and tried to commit suicide one day by taking a lot of pills. He came down to the station in bad shape and Ellie called the ambulance—she, she was always trying to help people. Somehow he fixated on her, although she wasn't interested in him. In fact, she'd become frightened and had been avoiding him. He'd had a problem back in New Mexico where he was suspected of embezzling some racetrack funds and received a court order to return for trial. Some of the locals (including Ellie) thought he was innocent and had gotten up a petition to combat the charge.

"On the day of the attack, he'd been drinking in the local bars and asking about her. He reported in a newspaper interview that he had to leave for New Mexico and he came to tell her good-bye. She was alone in the radio station (not uncommon for such a small station) for the late afternoon shift. Apparently he was drunk and abusive and Ellie called his mother on the phone (she was working around the corner at the Silver King Bakery) to come and get him out of the station. At this point, Ellie must have put on the headphones and gone back on the air thinking he had gone. We'll never know the exact sequence of action but presume that was when he attacked her. He grabbed a hammer that had been lying on the counter and struck her from behind. He hit her head repeatedly, breaking her skull in many places."

"What?" He pressed his hand to his temple. "He did what?"

"Do I have to repeat it?"

"I need to hear it all."

"He struck her head many times and then her feet. From behind because Ellie was proficient in Tae Kwon Do and was strong. She told me later that she was ashamed that she couldn't defend herself from such a coward and a wimp.

"We don't know how long she lay there, but Garrett (another radio station employee) noticed that the radio station was off the air. He came to the station to check and found her lying unconscious in a large pool of dried blood. There were signs of a struggle and the operating cords were in a tangle around her feet.

"When the attack was discovered, everyone in town, including the Sheriff, immediately guessed it was Harmon. Why didn't *someone* stop him earlier?" My voice is getting high and squeaky. I take a deep breath so I can continue. "They went right to his mother's house and found him hiding in a closet. He was arrested and never tried to deny the charges. The only justification he gave was that Ellie threw a can of soda at him when he went in to tell her good-bye. When I asked her about this, she laughed and replied that it was against the rules to have any drinks in the operating area. She didn't even drink sodas." I stopped. I felt the familiar waves of shock and anger. I wished I were the one on an astral journey.

"Tell me the rest of it." His eyes were solemn.

"And the mother. I've never been able to understand why his mother didn't come to the radio station. Ellie called her at her bakery job around the corner and said that Frank was drunk and causing a problem at the radio station. And the psychiatrist that was treating him must have had some knowledge of his intentions. In a deposition the psychiatrist did say that Harmon was possibly violent and obsessed with Ellie.

"Anyway, that's the story." I gulp water from my paper cup. I feel my usual helpless feeling when I tell Ellie's story. What could I have done differently? And why didn't Harmon's mother come and get him out of the radio station when Ellie called her? "Is there anything you can to do help her? She's afraid a lot."

"We have to examine him."

"Him? But I don't want—anything for him."

"To help her. What's his full name?" he asked as he turned to the easel.

"Frank, Frank Harmon," I state his name matter-of-factly when I really want to scream it.

"Okay, let's examine the astral body of Frank. We'll talk about the 'Law of Ten.'" He begins to make a chart on the easel. He writes 'Law of Ten,' in red ink. In reference to Frank and his past lives he uses purple ink. And Else Ane's name he writes in blue ink.

His words flow smoothly. "His bad karma begins Dec. 13,1849, when he was a young woman named Jo." His face is serious and his eyes draw me in. "At fifteen, she was raped, beaten and abused, which caused twelve units of psychic energy. Next, she was born as a man, then as woman and then again as Frank Harmon in 1958. These lives accumulated, because of the 'Law of Ten,' 120 negative units of psychic energy."

"He had multiple lives? All bad ones?"

"Yes." He writes 'The Furious & Tortured' on the chart. "His characteristics are disapproval, self-hate, anger and fury. His soul is full of grief, shame, and sense of loss."

"He's in prison and I don't want anything to do with him." I feel my voice getting shrill. "It's my daughter that needs help. She can barely read or write—"

"I understand. But we have to work through him."

"Okay." I take a deep breath. "Let's do it then."

He goes to the kitchen. Through the door I notice the maple cabinets, tile counters, stainless steel appliances and slate floor. He rummages in the cabinets and came back with a clear plastic bag full of a white, soft material. Next, he massages the plastic bag with his strong hand—his brow furrows and his shoulders hunch.

I wonder if it is cornstarch in the bag.

"I ask for healing, for approval of the castrated, worthless astral body of Frank." As he molds the bag with his strong hands, I picture him restoring Ellie's head to its former smooth condition.

"Remove the vulnerable, dead, stultified feelings from astral body of Frank."

He bends his head as if in prayer and I study his thinning hair and stooped shoulders. When he looks up his brow is smooth and his hands are finally still.

"Should I take that?" I gestured to the bag.

"I'll dispose of the waste—it's all in here. You can have the chart."

I fold the chart and stuff it in my purse. "Thank you." I feel like hugging him but do a handshake instead. "Thank you very much." Although money hasn't been mentioned, I write him a check for fifty dollars and leave it on the kitchen table.

I'm calm as we drive home. I feel light like after a long night's sleep. Or like the time one of my friends hypnotized me—as if I had been away and come back refreshed. The sun is just dipping behind the Coastal Range and the dark almond branches reach for the last light. It's one of those rare times when there's no traffic on Highway 99.

"How was your session?" Annetta asks." The car is so quiet her words glide toward me as if over water.

"Good, I think—hard to know."

"What do you mean—you don't know? How do you feel?"

"I feel like I accomplished something. But I don't feel like I can talk about it," I laugh, "it might disappear."

"That's okay. I feel like I did good work too—letting go of big chunks of things. Was your session about Ellie?"

"Yes. I have a chart he worked out." I point to my purse.

"I have a chart, too. That's seems to be how he works—on any subject. I noticed that half of the pad on the easel was gone."

"Did you pay anything?" I ask. "How do you know how much or if you should pay at all?"

"I gave him a check. Did you see his sweater? It was worn out. And he needed a haircut."

"Yes, I noticed. He seemed sincere, didn't he?"

"Oh, he's for real. Carla and Scott sponsor him all the time." She pats my hand. "I'm glad we went together."

As soon as I get home I put the chart in the box with her medical records. Should I tell Ellie about the session? Maybe I shouldn't bring up the attack or Frank Harmon—remind her of what we all are trying to forget. I ponder but in the end say nothing to her. Gradually my feeling of accomplishment from the session fades. Two weeks go by and I stop thinking about the astral body of Frank, his multiple bad lives, and the chart with the purple words.

I do call Ellie every couple of days. It's hard to catch her at the house where she rents a room but I keep trying. Her days are long—she rides the bus every day to Santa Rosa Community College and takes classes and works with her tutors. Last Friday she seemed happy when we talked.

"You sound good," I say, "are you liking your classes?"

"Hard work. But I'm going to study—forestry."

"That sounds perfect for you. You could be a forest ranger."

"It will take a long time. But I will try to get into Humboldt State."

"I'm so proud of you for working so hard. Do you have a good scribe?"

"Yes, his name is—Todd. But Mom, the best thing has happened. Those bad night things, I don't have them anymore. Those—nightmares about being hurt."

"When did they stop?" I ask.

"They just stopped—about two weeks ago."

"Amazing. That's when I went to the psychic."

"Who?"

"A psychic. Remember my friend, Annetta? Well, we both went to see Clifton, that's the psychic's name, at her friend's home in Stockton. I talked to him about your injury. He said we had to remove the bad feelings from Frank to help you. He massaged a bag and used a chart to explain everything. I'll show you the chart the when you're home. Frank had had bad feelings stored up from all of his multiple lives. He was even a woman in one of his multiple lives, a woman who had been raped and beaten. Sounds weird, doesn't it? But I thought it was worth a try."

"It worked." She laughed. "My bad night dreams are gone. How did he do that? I don't even know him."

"He just said he had to remove the bad feelings from Frank."

"Frank—that—that coward! Why should we help him?"

"Only because we had to go through him to help you. And we did help you. Your nightmares are gone."

17

Everything Changes

Subj: no jobs
Date: Sept. 8, 2000

What kind of book are you writing about me? I ride my bike to the library but closed again. Our county can't pay each day. I got the dried cherries you sent home with me, the unsulphered so I'm not allergic. I had a turkey burger with white cheese for lunch. Thanks for that food. Did I tell you my counselor said there are no all time jobs in forestry even tho I have college degree?

Rain and then it rain again.

Subj: test
Date: Sept. 20, 2000

I take a test at a special doctor for the Social Security today. It's the same test as last time but I still can't finish it in the right time. I have to bring the bank papers too. They want to know how I spend the whole $600 every month.

I get the pictures of baby Ingrid. It's nice to be Aunt Ellie.

Once started, the details of Ellie's brain injury flow onto the pages. The writing is painful as I dredge the past for details but I feel I'm honoring Ellie as I write each page. Almost daily, as I am remembering and recording her story, I receive the emails from Ellie. They tell of her everyday struggles to live with a disability. And they display her humor and wisdom. Why not incorporate them into the book? It would be our book—my narrative and her emails. I like the idea of getting her own words in the book. Should I tell her I'm using them? Will she edit her them, get self-conscious, stop emailing me? For now I don't tell her I'm recording her emails. I just put my head down and type steadily hoping I'll know what to do when the time comes.

———————

Subj: asleep again
Date: October 15, 2000

Glad you are slowly getting over that cold. Those sinus headaches seem to get more painful at night somehow.

My hospice person sleep more of the time with me today. Once I ask her if she wants some coffee and she says yes and I went to get some. When I came back she was asleep again.

Is it time for me to read the book? What if Frank Harmon sees it and tries to find me?

Each day I watch for the mail truck. From my second floor study I can spy on my own mailbox. It's been about three weeks since I sent out twelve query letters. I know my chances are slim. What do I hope for anyway? Mostly for Ellie —if the book sells she'd have some income, the best outcome. Her story could help other brain injury victims—a million each year, of which 200,000 cause permanent disabilities. Each victim has a mother, father, siblings, and friends—all affected. Hers was a good recovery—not complete but a miracle. I want the world to know her, her courage.

Today I receive two letters from agents. One wants to see more chapters, one requests a proposal.

It's time.

Subject: bike Haiku
Date: October 20, 2000

I got the disc you send in the mail. It is a high heat of 56 now, which
is nice with the sun, the 35F this morning was a bit to cool. Here is
my Haiku that I'm entering in the contest.

Hour to reach distant sun,
Eighteen minutes flying to fog and mist,
Hoping for one more road-dance.

The phone rings. Ellie is incoherent. She yells and swears. "You stole my
emails, I hate you, you ******, you didn't tell me, I hate you." She is throwing
things, kicking, pounding, I try to calm her down. She hangs up on me then
calls me back with more of the raging. I no longer expect such severe emotional
outbursts from her. I call Andy. He calls her and gets the same screaming. What
should I do, I ask him? I decide to call tomorrow. I try to go on with dinner and a
meeting at the poetry center. Driving home I look up just in time to see my car two
inches away from the stopped truck in front of me. I'm sick with guilt and worry.

The next morning she doesn't answer. I'm pacing the house. I know she's
afraid of Harmon. I think of her suicide try. As the day goes on, I vacuum, wash
my car, scrub the toilets. A couple of times I get my car keys and purse and head
to the garage. Should I jump in the car and go to her? It's a six-hour drive. I call
Lars and Josie. They haven't heard from her either. I have a friend I worked with in
California Poets in the Schools who lives near. I explain the situation to him. Can
he go over? He equivocates—he has to teach tomorrow. Okay, I say, just forget it,
thinking, forget you too. I call the sheriff in her county. "My daughter is in danger,"
I convince them. She's had a brain injury and tried to hurt herself before. Can you
check out her apartment?" They promise to respond to my hysterical pleas. I wait
hours by the phone.

Finally, the sheriff calls. "She's okay. We told her to call you." That's all
they will say.

A week later I call Lars and Josie again. She has talked to them saying I had
no right to use her e-mails, she'll never forgive me.

The price is too high for this book. I'm Ellie's closest family member. What will she do without me? She needs me and I need her. I look at the letters from the agents. I know the book is good, I know her story is dramatic and inspiring, but I know it's not worth the loss of our relationship, nothing is. I open my laptop and write to her. "I'll forget the book. It's not worth it. If you don't want it published I'll respect your wishes. Forgive me for using your emails without telling you. I'll keep them forever but won't show them to anyone."

After I mail the letter, I give up for now. Give up on calling and writing emails to Ellie. She'll need time to digest and process. It's up to her now. I begin other writing projects but miss working on *Blue Shy*. Writing my narrative, incorporating her emails in the manuscript made me feel as if I was doing something for her, saving her words and daily experience.

I do think what it would be like for others to read and benefit from her story, maybe parents living with a brain-injured child. In fact, I hear from an old family friend, Sue, who has heard about Ellie and has a brain injury in her family, too. Once my babysitter in Eastern Montana, Sue now lives near Laramie, Wyoming, on a ranch. Her grandson, Joe, was injured during a football game. Flown by helicopter to a nearby trauma center, his life was saved but his recovery slow and his brain injury was permanent. Sue assists Joe during the day while his mother works. He is trying to finish high school.

In this bleak time of missing Ellie, (it's been about two months since I've heard from her) I'm comforted by Sue's response and our connection. Instead of emailing Ellie and working on *Blue Shy* I put my energy into my correspondence with Sue. I feel like I can talk to her. I tell her the general details of Ellie's injury, about her recovery and mention the book. Sue writes back immediately saying she wants to read it. I send the first twenty pages of *Blue Shy*. She loves the book, says it gave her hope, says she would love to meet Ellie. I don't actually tell her that I'm not hearing from Ellie. Instead I send her a little more of the book. Wait for her next letter. Wait for something from Ellie.

Subj: never
Date: Dec 11, 2000

Mom,
I guess I forgive you. You must never, never, never give my emails
to anyone. Don't send the book to anyone anymore. Not ever.

Ellie

In December we start to make plans for Christmas. Ellie and I have been
communicating for only a short time since the big fight. We talk on the phone
but I still don't get emails. Except for the one in December forgiving me. It's the
only email she's sent me that was signed Ellie, instead of Love, Ellie. We decide she
should drive to our house and the three of us, Andy, Ellie and I, will drive to her
brother's house in Oregon for the holiday. Pack your ski clothes, I say, we are only
a short drive from Mt. Bachelor.

The three of us have a rough trip up to Oregon. We get stranded just south
of Lake Shasta and have to wait for the snowplows to clear the roads. We're trapped
in the car for hours when Andy broaches the subject. "That *Blue Shy* is some great
book. I'd like to see it in the waiting rooms at the hospital. It would be inspiring
reading. I'd like to give it to my surgeon friends."

"You liked it? All those gory things that happened to me?" Ellie is calm.
"My wrong spelling and everything?"

"I didn't like that you were hurt. But the hospital reports made the book
more real. Your spelling is creative but your errors could be corrected. Didn't your
Mom tell you I'm a terrible speller? I think it is because I learned to sight read
instead of sounding out the words. I have your Mom or my secretary check my
writing." Andy says.

"Or you could just use spell check on the computer," Ellie suggests.

"Good idea." Andy pats my hand. I relax. I have been quiet and nervous
during this discussion.

It's a memorable Christmas. Two-year-old Ingrid pads around wearing
only a diaper and her wispy blonde hair. She hides her head under my arm when

Andy gets out his guitar and starts singing "Ole, Ole, Anna." By the next song she puts her hand on the strings of the guitar to make her own music. Ellie sticks the Christmas bows to her hair. Ellie's braids are thick and brown again. She's wrapped all her Christmas gifts with foil-covered candy kisses stuck to the packages. Ingrid pries them off, peels the foil and licks the chocolate. We all go cross-country skiing with my son toting Ingrid in a special backpack. He and Ellie race ahead of us with long strides then backtrack to accompany us.

Driving home to California Ellie leans over my seat. "That was a fun time, Mom."

"For me, too. Let's do it every Christmas."

The car is quiet for miles. Andy patiently drives just above the 55 mph Oregon speed limit. I look back at Ellie. She's listening to an opera on tape. I glance at the CD cover—the opera is *Eugene Onegin*. I gesture for her to remove her headphones. "I just had an idea," I say. "What about if I change all the names, the places, the dates in your book? That way no one would recognize you."

"All of them?"

"Yes," I promise.

"What about the emails?" Ellie asks. "I don't want people to see my weird writing."

"I love the emails, you're such a great writer. They make the book! But I could correct most of the spelling and the grammar."

"Okay," Ellie says. "I guess it's okay if people don't know it's about me." She leans back in the seat and puts on her headphones.

It's starting to snow. On the horizon to the right is snowcapped Mt. Jefferson. My feet are hot so I remove my snow boots and massage my toes. I scrapple in my purse for a pen and pull out an old grocery list. On the back I write some new names for family members. I search for just the right tone. Names that will fit and conceal. I'm excited about the new story.

Subj: sun
Date: Dec. 31, 2000

Hi Mom,

The sky turned dark about 1 PM and it started to rain very hard but
now it is 4:30 and the storm is blowing away; so with the clouds
and the sunsetting sun all the trees have become yellow-gold

Love, Ellie

blue shy

Epilogue

Ellie has made a remarkable recovery from her brain injury, thanks to the expertise of the doctors who mended her physically, the therapists who patiently helped her regain her language skills, and the counselors who helped her through her despair and to regain her spirit. Our tears aren't over; we, her family and friends, will always be saddened by Ellie's tragedy. But we are grateful for her recovery, for her life, for the person she has grown into: humorous, compassionate, wise, and intellectually curious.

With the help of tutors provided by our California college system, and her own hard work and persistence, she graduated with a BA in Forestry. She lives on her own, completely independent, and is able to handle all her financial affairs—even the difficulties of working with the Social Security system. Unable to work full time because of her ongoing cognitive disabilities, she gives generously of herself as a volunteer for Hospice and at an elementary school library. Physically very active, she hikes, skis and is an avid bicyclist.

The names, dates and places in this book have been changed to protect Ellie's anonymity. All proceeds from the sale of *Blue Shy* will go directly to a special needs trust fund set up for Ellie, and a portion to the Brain Injury Association of America.

blue shy

TBI INCIDENCE

Every 23 seconds one person in the US sustains a Traumatic Brain Injury. An estimated 5.3 Americans, a little more than 2 % of the US population, currently live with disabilities resulting from Traumatic Brain Injury. 1.4 million Americans sustain a Traumatic Brain Injury each year and more than 50,000 people die. Brain injury affects 35 times more people than HIV/AIDS, 9 times more people than breast cancer.

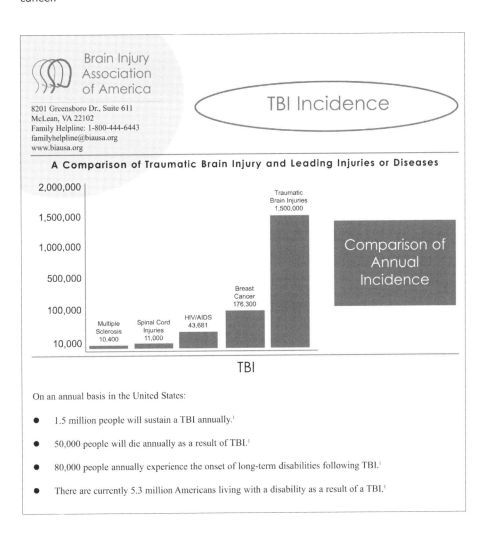

Brain Injury Association of America

8201 Greensboro Dr., Suite 611
McLean, VA 22102
Family Helpline: 1-800-444-6443
familyhelpline@biausa.org
www.biausa.org

TBI Incidence

A Comparison of Traumatic Brain Injury and Leading Injuries or Diseases

Comparison of Annual Incidence

- Multiple Sclerosis 10,400
- Spinal Cord Injuries 11,000
- HIV/AIDS 43,681
- Breast Cancer 176,300
- Traumatic Brain Injuries 1,500,000

TBI

On an annual basis in the United States:

- 1.5 million people will sustain a TBI annually.[1]

- 50,000 people will die annually as a result of TBI.[1]

- 80,000 people annually experience the onset of long-term disabilities following TBI.[1]

- There are currently 5.3 million Americans living with a disability as a result of a TBI.[1]

Source: Traumatic Brian Injury.com

GLASGOW COMA SCALE

There are a few different systems that medical practitioners use to diagnose the symptoms of Traumatic Brain Injury. The Glasgow Coma Scale is based on a 15 point scale for estimating and categorizing the outcomes of brain injury on the basis of overall social capability or dependence on others.

The test measures the motor response, verbal response and eye opening response with these values:

I. Motor Response

6 - Obeys commands fully
5 - Localizes to noxious stimuli
4 - Withdraws from noxious stimuli
3 - Abnormal flexion, i.e. decorticate posturing
2 - Extensor response, i.e. decerebrate posturing
1 - No response

II. Verbal Response

5 - Alert and Oriented
4 - Confused, yet coherent, speech
3 - Inappropriate words and jumbled phrases consisting of words
2 - Incomprehensible sounds
1 - No sounds

III. Eye Opening

4 - Spontaneous eye opening
3 - Eyes open to speech
2 - Eyes open to pain
1 - No eye opening

The final score is determined by adding the values of I+II+III.

This number helps medical practitioners categorize the four possible levels for survival, with a lower number indicating a more severe injury and a poorer prognosis:

Mild (13-15)
- Loss of consciousness less than 30 minutes
- Most prevalent TBI
- Also known as concussion, minor head trauma, minor brain injury
- Often missed at time of initial injury
- Symptoms include headache, difficulty thinking, memory problems, attention deficits, mood swings and frustration; in 15% of people symptoms can last one year or more

Moderate Disability (9-12):
- Loss of consciousness greater than 30 minutes
- Physical or cognitive impairments which may or may not resolve
- Benefit from Rehabilitation

Severe Disability (3-8):
- Coma: unconscious state. No meaningful response, no voluntary activities

Vegetative State (Less Than 3):
- Sleep wake cycles
- Arousal, but no interaction with environment
- No localized response to pain

Persistent Vegetative State:
- Vegetative state lasting longer than one month

Brain Death:
- No brain function
- Specific criteria needed for making this diagnosis

Source: TRAUMATIC BRAIN INJURY.COM

ASESSMENT SCALES: Levels of Cognitive Functioning

Level I – No Response
Patient appears to be in a deep sleep and is completely unresponsive to any stimuli presented to him.

Level II – Generalized Response
Patient reacts inconsistently and non-purposefully to stimuli in a non-specific manner. limited in nature and are often the same regardless of stimulus presented. Responses may be physiological changes, gross body movements, and/or vocalization. Often, the earliest response is to deep pain. Responses are likely to be delayed.

Level III – Localized Response
Patient reacts specifically, but inconsistently, to stimuli. The patient may withdraw an extremity and/or vocalize when presented with a painful stimulus. He may follow simple commands in an inconsistent manner. He may also show a vague awareness of self and body by responding to discomfort by pulling at nasogastric tube or catheter.

Level IV – Confused/Agitated
Patient is in a heightened state of activity with severely decreased ability to process information. He is detached from the present and responds primarily to his own confusion. Behavior is frequently bizarre and non-purposeful. Verbalization if frequently incoherent and inappropiate to the environment. Confabulation may be present; he may be euphoric or hostile. He is unable to perform self-care (feeding, dressing) with maximum assistance.

Level V – Confused, Inappropriate Non-Agitated
Patient appears alert and is able to respond to simple commands, however with increased complexity of commands responses are random and fragmented. He has gross attention to the environment, but is highly distractible and lacks ability to focus. Management on the ward is often a problem if the patient is physically mobile, as he may wander off, either randomly or with vague intentions of going home.

Level VI - Confused, Appropriate
Patient shows goal-directed behavior, but is dependent on external input for direction. He follows simple directions. He is at least supervised with old learning. Past memories show more depth and detail than recent memory.

Level VII – Automatic, Appropriate

Patient appears appropriate and oriented within hospital, goes through daily routine automatically, but frequently robot-like. He has superficial awareness of, but lacks insight into, his condition, decreased judgment and problem solving and lacks realistic planning for his future. He in independent in self-care activities and supervised in home and community skills for safety. His judgment remains impaired; such that he is unable to drive a car. Prevocational or avoctional evaluation and counseling may be indicated.

Level VIII – Purposeful, Appropriate

Patient is alert and oriented, is able to recall and integrate past and recent events, and is aware of, and responsive to his culture. Within his physical capabilities, he is independent in home and community skills. Vocational rehabilitation to determine his ability to return a contributor to society is indicated. He may continue to show a decreased ability, relative to premorbid abilities, in abstract reasoning, tolerance for stress, judgment in emergencies or unusual circumstances. His social, emotional, and intellectual capacities may continue to be at a decreased level for him, but functional in society.

Source: Bay Area Head Injury Recovery Center

blue shy

Author

Barbara Link received her MA in creative writing from Mills College in Oakland. Her powerful memoir, *Blue Shy*, was awarded first prize in the Sacramento Friends of the Library first chapter contest, and excerpts have been published in *Kaleidoscope, American River Review* and *CORIL Newsletter* (Central Oregon Resources for Independent Living). She is also a co-author of *Coffee and Ink*, a manual for writing groups. Her fiction and poetry have appeared in numerous literary magazines, and in 2008 she received the Bazzanella Prize at

Sacramento State University for graduate fiction. KVPR, a National Public Radio affiliate, has aired three of her short stories on *Valley Writers Read*. Barbara lives and writes in Sacramento, California.

Cover Artist—John Karl Claes was born and raised in the San Joaquin Valley of California. He completed a B.A. in studio art at California State University, Stanislaus and then earned a M.F.A. in painting and drawing from the University of North Carolina, Greensboro. He shows in galleries throughout the country including Sacramento, San Francisco and Chicago. He currently lives in California's Central Valley with his wife and two sons, where he also maintains his studio. To learn more about the artist and his work, visit his website at www.johnkarlclaes.com.